Principles

Principles

AN ANTHOLOGY OF READINGS

Selected by Jane Syburg

FIDES PUBLISHERS, INC.
NOTRE DAME, INDIANA

Preface

The literature in *Principles* was selected to explore the question "What do I stand for?" The selections take the reader into a variety of situations, all of which are closely related to everyday life.

The readings do not attempt to answer the thematic question. They merely indicate a need for the reader to answer it. Though the readings were selected to relate to young adults, the literature and the principles are by no means confined to that age group. The need to have a set of principles is both ageless and timeless.

January, 1969   Jane Syburg

Contents

THE BLOOD OF THE MARTYRS   9
STEPHEN VINCENT BENÉT

TWO SOLDIERS   28
WILLIAM FAULKNER

MY CHRISTMAS CAROL   45
BUDD SCHULBERG

CATHERINE AND THE WINTER WHEAT   55
P. B. HUGHES

IMPULSE   60
CONRAD AIKEN

AMERICAN DISGRACE: COLLEGE CHEATING   74
JEROME ELLISON

THE HERO   86
MARGARET WEYMOUTH JACKSON

STRANGERS IN TOWN   102
SHIRLEY JACKSON

LOVE AND A QUESTION   118
ROBERT FROST

SHEENER   120
BEN AMES WILLIAMS

NIGGER HORSE   131
F. K. FRANKLIN

THE ROCKING-HORSE WINNER   148
D. H. LAWRENCE

FIFTY-TWO MILES TO TERROR   166
ALEX GABY

EXCERPTS FROM FAREWELL ADDRESS AND
"CIVIL DISOBEDIENCE"   181
GEORGE WASHINGTON AND HENRY DAVID THOREAU

BAD CALL   182
RICHARD VINCENT

A GLASS OF BLESSINGS   198
GLENDON SWARTHOUT

DUSKY RUTH   207
A. E. COPPARD

A SHOWER OF GOLD   217
DONALD BARTHELME

A WHITE HERON   227
SARAH ORNE JEWETT

LITTLE JESS AND THE OUTRIDER   239
JESSAMYN WEST

THE BEAR   262
WILLIAM FAULKNER

STEPHEN VINCENT BENET

The Blood of the Martyrs

The man who expected to be shot lay with his eyes open, staring at the upper left-hand corner of his cell. He was fairly well over his last beating, and they might come for him any time now. There was a yellow stain in the cell corner near the ceiling; he had liked it at first, then disliked it; now he was coming back to liking it again.

He could see it more clearly with his glasses on, but he put on his glasses only for special occasions now—the first thing in the morning, and when they brought the food in, and for interviews with the General. The lenses of the glasses had been cracked in a beating some months before, and it strained his eyes to wear them too long. Fortunately, in his present life he had very few occasions demanding clear vision. But, nevertheless, the accident to his glasses worried him, as it worries all near-sighted people. You put your glasses on the first thing in the morning, and the world leaps into proportion; if it does not do so, something is wrong with the world.

9

The man did not believe greatly in symbols, but his chief nightmare nowadays was an endless one in which, suddenly and without warning, a large piece of glass would drop out of one of the lenses and he would grope around the cell, trying to find it. He would grope very carefully and gingerly, for hours of darkness, but the end was always the same—the small, unmistakable crunch of irreplaceable glass beneath his heel or his knee. Then he would wake up sweating, with his hands cold. This dream alternated with the one of being shot, but he found no great benefit in the change.

As he lay there, you could see that he had an intellectual head—the head of a thinker or a scholar, old and bald, with the big, domed brow. It was, as a matter of fact, a well-known head; it had often appeared in the columns of newspapers and journals, sometimes when the surrounding text was in a language Professor Malzius could not read. The body, though stooped and worn, was still a strong peasant body and capable of surviving a good deal of ill-treatment, as his captors had found out. He had fewer teeth than when he came to prison, and both the ribs and the knee had been badly set, but these were minor matters. It also occurred to him that his blood count was probably poor. However, if he could ever get out and to a first-class hospital, he was probably good for at least ten years more of work. But, of course, he would not get out. They would shoot him before that, and it would be over.

Sometimes he wished passionately that it would be over—tonight—this moment; at other times he was shaken by the mere blind fear of death. The latter he tried to treat as he would have treated an attack of malaria, knowing that it was an attack, but not always with success. He should have been able to face it better than most—he was Gregor Malzius, the scientist—but that did not always help. The fear of death persisted, even when one had noted and classified it as a purely physical reaction. When he was out of here, he would be able to write a very instructive little paper on the fear of death. He could even do it here, if he had writing materials, but there was no use asking for those.

Once they had been given to him, and he had spent two days quite happily. But they had torn up the work and spat upon it in front of his face. It was a childish thing to do, but it discouraged a man from working.

It seemed odd that he had never seen anybody shot, but he never had. During the war, his reputation and his bad eyesight had exempted him from active service. He had been bombed a couple of times when his reserve battalion was guarding the railway bridge, but that was quite different. You were not tied to a stake, and the airplanes were not trying to kill you as an individual. He knew the place where it was done here, of course. But prisoners did not see the executions, they merely heard, if the wind was from the right quarter.

He had tried again and again to visualize how it would be, but it always kept mixing with an old steel engraving he had seen in boyhood—the execution of William Walker, the American filibuster, in Honduras. William Walker was a small man with a white semi-Napoleonic face. He was standing, very correctly dressed, in front of an open grave, and before him a ragged line of picturesque natives were raising their muskets. When he was shot he would instantly and tidily fall into the grave, like a man dropping through a trap door; as a boy, the extreme neatness of the arrangement had greatly impressed Gregor Malzius. Behind the wall there were palm trees, and, somewhere off to the right, blue and warm, the Caribbean Sea. It would not be like that at all, for his own execution; and yet, whenever he thought of it, he thought of it as being like that.

Well, it was his own fault. He could have accepted the new regime; some respectable people had done that. He could have fled the country; many honorable people had. A scientist should be concerned with the eternal, not with transient political phenomena; and a scientist should be able to live anywhere. But thirty years at the university were thirty years and, after all, he was Malzius, one of the first biochemists in the world. To the last, he had not believed that they would touch him. Well, he had been wrong about that.

The truth, of course, was the truth. One taught it or one did not teach it. If one did not teach it, it hardly mattered what one did. But he had no quarrel with any established government; he was willing to run up a flag every Tuesday, as long as they let him alone. Most people were fools, and one government was as good as another for them—it had taken them twenty years to accept his theory of cell mutation. Now, if he'd been like his friend Bonnard—a fellow who signed protests, attended meetings for the cause of world peace, and generally played the fool in public—they'd have had some reason to complain. An excellent man in his field, Bonnard—none better—but outside of it, how deplorably like an actor, with his short gray beard, his pink cheeks, and his impulsive enthusiasm! Any government could put a fellow like Bonnard in prison—though it would be an injury to science and, therefore, wrong. For that matter, he thought grimly, Bonnard would enjoy being a martyr. He'd walk grace-fully to the execution post with a begged cigarette in his mouth, and some theatrical last quip. But Bonnard was safe in his own land—doubtless writing heated and generous articles on The Case of Professor Malzius—and he, Malzius, was the man who was going to be shot. He would like a cigarette, too, on his way to execution; he had not smoked in five months. But he certainly didn't intend to ask for one, and they wouldn't think of offering him any. That was the difference between him and Bonnard.

His mind went back with longing to the stuffy laboratory and stuffier lecture hall at the university; his feet yearned for the worn steps he had climbed ten thousand times, and his eyes for the long steady look through the truthful lens into worlds too tiny for the unaided eye. They had called him "The Bear" and "Old Prickly," but they had fought to work under him, the best of the young men. They said he would explain the Last Judg-ment in terms of cellular phenomena, but they had crowded to his lectures. It was Williams, the Englishman, who had made up the legend that he carried a choclate éclair and a set of improper post cards in his battered brief case. Quite untrue, of course— chocolate always made him ill, and he never looked at an improper post card in his life. And Williams would never know that he knew the legend, too; for Williams had been killed long ago in the war. For a moment, Professor Malzius felt blind hate at the thought of an excellent scientific machine like Williams being smashed in a war. But blind hate was an improper emotion for a scientist, and he put it aside.

He smiled grimly again; they hadn't been able to break up his classes—lucky he was The Bear! He'd seen one colleague hooted from his desk by a band of determined young hoodlums—too bad, but if a man couldn't keep order in his own classroom, he'd better get out. They'd wrecked his own laboratory, but not while he was there.

It was so senseless, so silly. "In God's name," he said reasonably, to no one, "what sort of conspirator do you think I would make? A man of my age and habits! I am interested in cellular phenomena!" And yet they were beating him because he would not tell about the boys. As if he had even paid attention to half the nonsense! There were certain passwords and greetings—a bar of music you whistled, entering a restaurant; the address of a firm that specialized, ostensibly, in vacuum cleaners. But they were not his own property. They belonged to the young men who had trusted The Bear. He did not know what half of them meant, and the one time he had gone to a meeting, he had felt like a fool. For they were fools and childish—playing the childish game of conspiracy that people like Bonnard enjoyed. Could they even make a better world than the present? He doubted it extremely. And yet, he could not betray them; they had come to him, looking over their shoulders, with darkness in their eyes.

A horrible, an appalling thing to be trusted. He had no wish to be a guide and counselor of young men. He wanted to do his work. Suppose they were poor and ragged and oppressed; he had been a peasant himself, he had eaten black bread. It was by his own efforts that he was Professor Malzius. He did not wish the confidences of boys like Gregopolous and the others—for, after all, what was Gregopolous? An excellent and untiring laboratory assistant—and a laboratory assistant he would remain to the end of his days. He had pattered about the laboratory like a fox terrier, with a fox terrier's quick, bright eyes. Like a devoted dog, he had made a god of Professor Malzius. "I don't want your problems, man. I don't want to know what you are doing outside the laboratory." But Gregopolous had brought his problems and his terrible trust none the less, humbly and proudly, like a fox terrier with a bone. After that—well, what was a man to do?

He hoped they would get it over with, and quickly. The world should be like a chemical formula, full of reason and logic. Instead there were all these young men, and their eyes. They conspired, hopelessly and childishly, for what they called freedom against the new regime. They wore no overcoats in winter and were often hunted and killed. Even if they did not conspire, they had miserable little love affairs and ate the wrong food—yes, even before, at the university, they had been the same. Why the devil would they not accept? Then they could do their work. Of course, a great many of them would not be allowed to accept —they had the wrong ideas or the wrong politics—but then they could run away. If Malzius, at twenty, had had to run from his country, he would still have been a scientist. To talk of a free world was a delusion; men were not free in the world. Those who wished got a space of time to get their work done. That was all. And yet, he had not accepted—he did not know why.

Now he heard the sound of steps along the corridor. His body began to quiver, and the places where he had been beaten hurt him. He noted it as an interesting reflex. Sometimes they merely flashed the light in the cell and passed by. On the other hand, it might be death. It was a hard question to decide.

The lock creaked, the door opened. "Get up, Malzius!" said the hard, bright voice of the guard. Gregor Malzius got up. A little stiffly, but quickly.

"Put on your glasses, you old fool!" said the guard, with a laugh. "You are going to the General."

Professor Malzius found the stone floors of the corridor uneven, though he knew them well enough. Once or twice the guard struck him, lightly and without malice, as one strikes an old horse with a whip. The blows were familiar and did not register on Professor Malzius' consciousness; he merely felt proud of not stumbling. He was apt to stumble; once he had hurt his knee. He noticed, it seemed to him, an unusual tenseness and officiousness about his guard. Once, even, in a brightly lighted corridor the guard moved to strike him, but refrained. However, that, too, happened occasionally, with one guard or another, and Professor Malzius merely noted the fact. It was a small fact, but an important one in the economy in which he lived.

But there could be no doubt that something unusual was going on in the castle. There were more guards than usual, many of them strangers. He tried to think, carefully, as he walked, if it could be one of the new national holidays. It was hard to keep track of them all. The General might be in a good humor. Then they would merely have a cat-and-mouse conversation for half an hour, and nothing really bad would happen. Once, even, there had been a cigar. Professor Malzius, the scientist, licked his lips at the thought.

Now he was being turned over to a squad of other guards, with salutings. This was really unusual; Professor Malzius bit his mouth inconspicuously. He had the poignant distrust of a monk or an old prisoner at any break in routine. Old prisoners are your true conservatives; they demand only that the order around them remain exactly the same.

It alarmed him as well that the new guards did not laugh at him. New guards almost always laughed when they saw him for the first time. He was used to the laughter and missed it—his throat felt dry. He would have liked, just once, to eat at the university restaurant before he died. It was bad food, ill-cooked and starchy, food good enough for poor students and professors, but he would have liked to be there, in the big smoky room that smelled of copper boilers and cabbage, with a small cup of bitter coffee before him and a cheap cigarette. He did not ask for his dog or his notebooks, the old photographs in his bedroom, his incomplete experiments or his freedom. Just to lunch once more at the university restaurant and have people point out The Bear. It seemed a small thing to ask, but of course it was quite impossible.

"Halt!" said a voice, and he halted. There were, for the third time, salutings. Then the door to the General's office opened, and he was told to go in.

He stood, just inside the door, in the posture of attention, as he had been taught. The crack in the left lens of his glasses made a crack across the room, and his eyes were paining him already, but he paid no attention to that. There was the familiar figure of the General, with his air of a well-fed and extremely healthy tomcat, and there was another man, seated at the General's desk. He could not see the other man very well—the crack made him bulge and waver—but he did not like his being there.

"Well, Professor," said the General, in an easy, purring voice. Malzius' entire body jerked. He had made a fearful, an unpardonable omission. He must remedy it at once. " Long live the state," he shouted in a loud thick voice, and saluted. He knew, bitterly, that his salute was ridiculous and that he looked ridiculous making it. But perhaps the General would laugh—he had done so before. Then everything would be all right, for it was not quite as easy to beat a man after you laughed at him.

The General did not laugh. He made a half turn instead, toward the man at the desk. The gesture said, "You see, he is well trained." It was the gesture of a man of the world, accustomed to deal with unruly peasants and animals—the gesture of a man fitted to be General.

The man at the desk paid no attention to the General's gesture. He lifted his head, and Malzius saw him more clearly and with complete unbelief. It was not a man but a picture come alive. Professor Malzius had seen the picture a hundred times; they had made him salute and take off his hat in front of it, when he had had a hat. Indeed, the picture had presided over his beatings. The man himself was a little smaller, but the picture was a good picture. There were many dictators in the world, and this was one type. The face was white, beaky and semi-Napoleonic;

the lean, military body sat squarely in its chair. The eyes dominated the face, and the mouth was rigid. I remember also a hypnotist, and a woman Charcot showed me, at his clinic in Paris, thought Professor Malzius. But there is also, obviously, an endocrine unbalance. Then his thoughts stopped.

"Tell the man to come closer," said the man at the desk. "Can he hear me? Is he deaf?"

"No, Your Excellency," said the General, with enormous, purring respect. "But he is a little old, though perfectly healthy. . . . Are you not, Professor Malzius?"

"Yes, I am perfectly healthy. I am very well treated here," said Professor Malzius, in his loud thick voice. They were not going to catch him with traps like that, not even by dressing up somebody as the Dictator. He fixed his eyes on the big old-fashioned inkwell on the General's desk—that, at least, was perfectly sane.

"Come closer," said the man at the desk to Professor Malzius, and the latter advanced till he could almost touch the inkwell with his fingers. Then he stopped with a jerk, hoping he had done right. The movement removed the man at the desk from the crack in his lenses, and Professor Malzius knew suddenly that it was true. This was indeed, the Dictator, this man with the rigid mouth. Professor Malzius began to talk.

"I have been very well treated here, and the General has acted with the greatest consideration," he said. "But I am Professor Gregor Malzius—professor of biochemistry. For thirty years I have lectured at the university; I am a fellow of the Royal Society, a corresponding member of the Academy of Sciences at Berlin, at Rome, at Boston, at Paris, and at Stockholm. I have received the Nottingham Medal, the Lamarck Medal, the Order of St. John of Portugal, and the Nobel Prize. I think my blood count is low, but I have received a great many degrees, and my experiments on the migratory cells are not finished. I do not wish to complain of my treatment, but I must continue my experiments."

He stopped, like a clock that has run down, surprised to hear the sound of his own voice. He noted, in one part of his mind, that the General had made a move to silence him, but had himself been silenced by the Dictator.

"Yes, Professor Malzius," said the man at the desk, in a harsh, toneless voice. "There has been a regrettable error." The rigid face stared at Professor Malzius. Professor Malzius stared back, He did not say anything.

"In these days," said the Dictator, his voice rising, "the nation demands the submission of every citizen. Encircled by jealous foes, our reborn land yet steps forward toward her magnificent destiny." The words continued for some time, the voice rose and fell. Professor Malzius listened respectfully; he had heard the words many times before, and they had ceased to have meaning to him. He was thinking of certain cells of the body that rebel against the intricate processes of Nature and set up their own bellicose state. Doubtless they, too, have a destiny, he thought, but in medicine it is called cancer.

"Jealous and spiteful tongues in other countries have declared that it is our purpose to wipe out learning and science," concluded the Dictator. "That is not our purpose. After the cleansing, the rebirth. We mean to move forward to the greatest science in the world—our own science, based on the enduring principles of our nationhood." He ceased abruptly, his eyes fell into their dream. Very like the girl Charcot showed me in my young days, thought Professor Malzius; there was first the ebullition, then the calm.

"I was part of the cleansing? You did not mean to hurt me?" he asked timidly.

"Yes, Professor Malzius," said the General, smiling, "you were part of the cleansing. Now that is over. His Excellency has spoken."

"I do not understand," said Professor Malzius, gazing at the fixed face of the man behind the desk.

"It is very simple," said the General. He spoke in a slow careful voice, as one speaks to a deaf man or a child. "You are a distinguished man of science—you have received the Nobel Prize,

That was a service to the state. You became, however, infected by the wrong political ideas. That was treachery to the state. You had, therefore, as decreed by His Excellency, to pass through a certain period for probation and rehabilitation. But that, we believe, is finished."

"You do not wish to know the names of the young men any more?" said Professor Malzius. "You do not want the addresses?"

"That is no longer of importance," said the General patiently. "There is no longer opposition. The leaders were caught and executed three weeks ago."

"There is no longer opposition," repeated Professor Malzius.

"At the trial, you were not even involved."

"I was not even involved," said Professor Malzius. "Yes."

"Now," said the General, with a look at the Dictator, "we come to the future. I will be frank—the new state is frank with its citizens."

"It is so," said the Dictator, his eyes still sunk in his dream.

"There has been—let us say—a certain agitation in foreign countries regarding Professor Malzius," said the General, his eyes still fixed on the Dictator. "That means nothing, of course. Nevertheless, your acquaintance, Professor Bonnard, and others have meddled in matters that do not concern them."

"They asked after me?" said Professor Malzius, with surprise. "It is true, my experiments were reaching a point that—"

"No foreign influence could turn us from our grim purpose," said the Dictator. "But it is our firm purpose to show our nation first in science and culture as we have already shown her first in manliness and statehood. For that reason, you are here, Professor Malzius." He smiled.

Professor Malzius stared. His cheeks began to tremble.

"I do not understand," said Professor Malzius. "You will give me my laboratory back?"

"Yes," said the Dictator, and the General nodded as one nods to a stupid child.

Professor Malzius passed a hand across his brow.

"My post at the university?" he said. "My experiments?"

"It is the purpose of our regime to offer the fullest encouragement to our loyal sons of science," said the Dictator.

"First of all," said Professor Malzius, "I must go to a hospital. My blood count is poor. But that will not take long." His voice had become impatient and his eyes glowed. "Then—my notebooks were burned, I suppose. I have a very good memory, an excellent memory. The theories are in my head, you know," and he tapped it. "I must have assistants, of course; little Gregopolous was my best one—"

"The man Gregopolous has been executed," said the General, in a stern voice. "You had best forget him."

"Oh," said Professor Malzius. "Well, then, I must have someone else. You see, these are important experiments. There must be some young men—clever ones—they cannot all be dead. I will know them." He laughed a little, nervously. "The Bear always got the pick of the crop," he said. "They used to call me The Bear, you know." He stopped and looked at them for a moment with ghastly eyes. "You are not fooling me?" he said. He burst into tears.

When he recovered he was alone in the room with the General. The General was looking at him as he himself had looked once at strange forms of life under the microscope, with neither disgust not attraction, but with great interest.

"His Excellency forgives your unworthy suggestion," he said. "He knows you are overwrought."

"Yes," said Professor Malzius. He sobbed once and dried his glasses.

"Come, come," said the General, with a certain bluff heartiness. "We mustn't have our new president of the National Academy crying. It would look badly in the photographs."

"President of the Academy?" said Professor Malzius quickly. "Oh, no; I mustn't be that. They make speeches; they have administrative work. But I am a scientist, a teacher."

"I'm afraid you can't very well avoid it," said the General, still heartily, though he looked at Professor Malzius. "Your induction will be quite a ceremony. His Excellency himself will preside. And you will speak on the new glories of our science. It will be a magnificent answer to the petty and jealous criticisms of our neighbors. Oh, you needn't worry about the speech," he added quickly. "It will be prepared; you will only have to read it. His Excellency thinks of everything."

"Very well," said Professor Malzius, "and then may I go back to my work?"

"Oh, don't worry about that," said the General, smiling. "I'm only a simple soldier; I don't know about those things. But you'll have plenty of work."

"The more the better," said Malzius eagerly. "I still have ten good years."

He opened his mouth to smile, and a shade of dismay crossed the General's face.

"Yes," he said, as if to himself. "The teeth must be attended to. At once. And a rest, undoubtedly, before the photographs are taken. Milk. You are feeling sufficiently well, Professor Malzius?"

"I am very happy," said Professor Malzius. "I have been very well treated, and I come of peasant stock."

"Good," said the General. He paused for a moment and spoke in a more official voice.

"Of course, it is understood, Professor Malzius—" he said.

"Yes?" said Professor Malzius. "I beg your pardon. I was thinking of something else."

"It is understood, Professor Malzius," repeated the General, "that your—er—rehabilitation in the service of the state is a permanent matter. Naturally, you will be under observation, but, even so, there must be no mistake."

"I am a scientist," said Professor Malzius impatiently. "What have I to do with politics? If you wish me to take oaths of loyalty, I will take as many as you wish."

"I am glad you take that attitude," said the General, though he looked at Professor Malzius curiously. "I may say that I regret the unpleasant side of our interviews. I trust you bear no ill will."

"Why should I be angry?" said Professor Malzius. "You were

told to do one thing. Now you are told to do another. That is all."

"It is not quite so simple as that," said the General rather stiffly. He looked at Professor Malzius for a third time. "And I'd have sworn you were one of the stiff-necked ones," he said. "Well, well, every man has his breaking point, I suppose. In a few moments you will receive the final commands of His Excellency. Tonight you will go to the capitol and speak over the radio. You will have no difficulty there—the speech is written. But it will put a quietus on the activities of our friend Bonnard and the question that has been raised in the British Parliament. Then a few weeks of rest by the sea and the dental work, and then, my dear president of the National Academy, you will be ready to undertake your new duties. I congratulate you and hope we shall meet often under pleasant auspices." He bowed from the waist to Malzius, the bow of a man of the world, though there was still something feline in his mustache. Then he stood to attention, and Malzius, too, for the Dictator had come into the room.

"It is settled?" said the Dictator. "Good. Gregor Malzius, I welcome you to the service of the new state. You have cast your errors aside and are part of our destiny."

"Yes," said Professor Malzius, "I will be able to do my work now."

The Dictator frowned a little.

"You will not only be able to continue your invaluable researches," he said, "but you will also be able—and it will be a part of your duty—to further our national ideals. Our reborn nation must rule the world for the world's good. There is a fire within us that is not in other stocks. Our civilization must be extended everywhere. The future wills it. It will furnish the subject of your first discourse as president of the Academy."

"But," said Professor Malzius, in a low voice, "I am not a soldier. I am a biochemist. I have no experience in these matters you speak of."

The Dictator nodded. "You are a distinguished man of science," he said. "You will prove that our women must bear soldiers, our men abandon this nonsense of republics and democracies for trust in those born to rule them. You will prove by scientific law that certain races—our race in particular—are destined to rule the world. You will prove they are destined to rule by the virtues of war, and that war is part of our heritage."

"But," said Professor Malzius, "it is not like that. I mean," he said, "one looks and watches in the laboratory. One waits for a long time. It is a long process, very long. And then, if the theory is not proved, one discards the theory. That is the way it is done. I probably do not explain it well. But I am a biochemist; I do not know how to look for the virtues of one race against another, and I can prove nothing about war, except that it kills. If I said anything else, the whole world would laugh at me."

"Not one in this nation would laugh at you," said the Dictator.

"But if they do not laugh at me when I am wrong, there is no science," said Professor Malzius, knotting his brows. He paused. "Do not misunderstand me," he said earnestly. "I have ten years of good work left; I want to get back to my laboratory. But, you see, there are the young men—if I am to teach the young men."

He paused again, seeing their faces before him. There were many. There was Williams, the Englishman, who had died in the war, and little Gregopolous with the fox-terrier eyes. There were all who had passed through his classrooms, from the stupidest to the best. They had shot little Gregopolous for treason, but that did not alter the case. From all over the world they had come—he remembered the Indian student and the Chinese. They wore cheap overcoats, they were hungry for knowledge, they ate the bad, starchy food of the poor restaurants, they had miserable little love affairs and played childish games of politics, instead of doing their work. Nevertheless, a few were promising—all must be given the truth. It did not matter if they died, but they must be given the truth. Otherwise there could be no continuity and no science.

He looked at the Dictator before him—yes, it was a hysteric

face. He would know how to deal with it in his classroom—but such faces should not rule countries or young men. One was willing to go through a great many meaningless ceremonies in order to do one's work—wear a uniform or salute or be president of the Academy. That did not matter; it was part of the due to Caesar. But not to tell lies to young men on one's own subject. After all, they had called him The Bear and said he carried improper post cards in his brief case. They had given him their terrible confidence—not for love or kindness, but because they had found him honest. It was too late to change.

The Dictator looked sharply at the General. "I thought this had been explained to Professor Malzius," he said.

"Why, yes," said Professor Malzius. "I will sign any papers. I assure you I am not interested in politics—a man like myself, imagine! One state is as good as another. And I miss my tobacco —I have not smoked in five months. But, you see, one cannot be a scientist and tell lies."

He looked at the two men.

"What happens if I do not?" he said, in a low voice. But, looking at the Dictator, he had his answer. It was a fanatic face.

"Why, we shall resume our conversations, Professor Malzius," said the General, with a simper.

"Then I shall be beaten again," said Professor Malzius. He stated what he knew to be a fact.

"The process of rehabilitation is obviously not quite complete," said the General, "but perhaps, in time—"

"It will not be necessary," said Professor Malzius. "I cannot be beaten again." He stared wearily around the room. His shoulders straightened—it was so he had looked in the classroom when they had called him The Bear. "Call your other officers in," he said in a clear voice. "There are papers for me to sign. I should like them all to witness."

"Why—" said the General. "Why—" He looked doubtfully at the Dictator.

An expression of gratification appeared on the lean, semi-

Napoleonic face. A white hand, curiously limp, touched the hand of Professor Malzius.

"You will feel so much better, Gregor," said the hoarse, tense voice. "I am so very glad you have given in."

"Why, of course, I give in," said Gregor Malzius. "Are you not the Dictator? And besides, if I do not, I shall be beaten again. And I cannot—you understand?—I cannot be beaten again."

He paused, breathing a little. But already the room was full of other faces. He knew them well, the hard faces of the new regime. But youthful some of them too.

The Dictator was saying something with regard to receiving the distinguished scientist, Professor Gregor Malzius, into the service of the state.

"Take the pen," said the General in an undertone. "The inkwell is there, Professor Malzius. Now you may sign."

Professor Malzius stood, his fingers gripping the big, old-fashioned inkwell. It was full of ink—the servants of the Dictator were very efficient. They could shoot small people with the eyes of fox terriers for treason, but their trains arrived on time and their inkwells did not run dry.

"The state," he said, breathing. "Yes. But science does not know about states. And you are a little man—a little, unimportant man."

Then, before the General could stop him, he had picked up the inkwell and thrown it in the Dictator's face. The next moment the General's fist caught him on the side of the head, and he fell behind the desk to the floor. But lying there, through his cracked glasses, he could still see the grotesque splashes of ink on the Dictator's face and uniform, and the small cut above his eye where the blood was gathering. They had not fired; he had thought he would be too close to the Dictator for them to fire in time.

"Take that man out and shoot him. At once," said the Dictator in a dry voice. He did not move to wipe the stains from his uniform—and for that Professor Malzius admired him. They

rushed then, each anxious to be first. But Professor Malzius made
no resistance.

As he was being hustled along the corridors, he fell now and
then. On the second fall, his glasses were broken completely, but
that did not matter to him. They were in a great hurry, he
thought, but all the better—one did not have to think while one
could not see.

Now and then he heard his voice make sounds of discomfort,
but his voice was detached from himself. There was little Gregopolous—he could see him very plainly—and Williams, with his
fresh English coloring—and all the men whom he had taught.

He had given them nothing but work and the truth; they
had given him their terrible trust. If he had been beaten again,
he might have betrayed them. But he had avoided that.

He felt a last weakness—a wish that someone might know.
They would not, of course; he would have died of typhoid in
the castle, and there would be regretful notices in the newspapers. And then he would be forgotten, except for his work,
and that was as it should be. He had never thought much of
martyrs—hysterical people in the main. Though he'd like Bonnard to have known about the ink; it was in the coarse vein of
humor that Bonnard could not appreciate. But then, he was a
peasant; Bonnard had often told him so.

They were coming out into an open courtyard now; he felt
the fresh air of outdoors. "Gently," he said. "A little gently.
What's the haste?" But already they were tying him to the post.
Someone struck him in the face and his eyes watered. "A schoolboy covered with ink," he muttered through his lost teeth. "A
hysterical schoolboy too. But you cannot kill truth."

They were not good last words, and he knew that they were
not. He must try to think of better ones—not shame Bonnard.
But now they had a gag in his mouth; just as well, it saved him
the trouble.

His body ached, bound against the post, but his sight and his
mind were clearer. He could make out the evening sky, gray

with fog, the sky that belonged to no country, but to all the world.

He could make out the gray high buttress of the castle. They had made it a jail, but it would not always be a jail. Perhaps in time it would not even exist. But if a little bit of truth were gathered, that would always exist, while there were men to remember and rediscover it. It was only the liars and the cruel who always failed.

Sixty years ago, he had been a little boy, eating black bread and thin cabbage soup in a poor house. It had been a bitter life, but he could not complain of it. He had had some good teachers, and his students had called him The Bear.

The gag hurt his mouth—they were getting ready now. There had been a girl called Anna once; he had almost forgotten her. And his rooms had smelled a certain way and he had had a dog. It did not matter what they did with the medals. He raised his head and looked once more at the gray foggy sky. In a moment there would be no thought, but, while there was thought, one must remember and note. His pulse rate was lower than he would have expected and his breathing oddly even, but those were not the important things. The important thing was beyond, in the gray sky that had no country, in the stones of the earth and the feeble human spirit. The important thing was truth.

"Ready!" called the officer. "Aim! Fire!" But Professor Malzius did not hear the three commands of the officer. He was thinking about the young men.

WILLIAM FAULKNER

Two Soldiers

Me and Pete would go down to Old Man Killegrew's and listen to his radio. We would wait until after supper, after dark, and we would stand outside Old Man Killegrew's parlor window, and we could hear it because Old Man Killegrew's wife was deaf, and so he run the radio as loud as it would run, and so me and Pete could hear it plain as Old Man Killegrew's wife could, I reckon, even standing outside with the window closed.

And that night I said, "What? Japanese? What's a pearl harbor?" and Pete said, "Hush."

And so we stood there, it was cold, listening to the fellow in the radio talking, only I couldn't make no heads nor tails neither out of it. Then the fellow said that would be all for a while, and me and Pete walked back up the road to home, and Pete told me what it was. Because he was nigh twenty and he had done finished the Consolidated last June and he knowed a heap: about them Japanese dropping bombs on Pearl Harbor and that Pearl Harbor was across the water.

"Across what water?" I said. "Across that Government reservoy up at Oxford?"

"Naw," Pete said. "Across the big water. The Pacific Ocean."

We went home. Maw and pap was already asleep, and me and Pete laid in the bed, and I still couldn't understand where it was, and Pete told me again—the Pacific Ocean.

"What's the matter with you?" Pete said. "You're going on nine years old. You been in school now ever since September. Ain't you learned nothing yet?"

"I reckon we ain't got as fer as the Pacific Ocean yet," I said.

We was still sowing the vetch then that ought to been all finished by the fifteenth of November, because pap was still behind, just like he had been ever since me and Pete had knowed him. And we had firewood to git in, too, but every night me and Pete would go down to Old Man Killegrew's and stand outside his parlor window in the cold and listen to his radio; then we would come back home and lay in the bed and Pete would tell me what it was. That is, he would tell me for a while. Then he wouldn't tell me. It was like he didn't want to talk about it no more. He would tell me to shut up because he wanted to go to sleep, but he never wanted to go to sleep.

He would lay there, a heap stiller than if he was asleep, and it would be something, I could feel it coming out of him, like he was mad at me even, only I knowed he wasn't thinking about me, or like he was worried about something, and it wasn't that neither, because he never had nothing to worry about. He never got behind like pap, let alone stayed behind. Pap give him ten acres when he graduated from the Consolidated, and me and Pete both reckoned pap was durn glad to get shut of at least ten acres, less to have to worry with himself; and Pete had them ten acres all sowed to vetch and busted out and bedded for the winter, and so it wasn't that. But it was something. And still we would go down to Old Man Killegrew's every night and listen to his radio, and they was at it in the Philippines now, but General MacArthur was holding um. Then we would come back home and lay in the bed, and Pete wouldn't tell me nothing or talk at all. He would just lay there still as a ambush and when I would touch him, his side or his leg would feel hard and still as iron, until after a while I would go to sleep.

Then one night—it was the first time he had said nothing to me except to jump on me about not chopping enough wood at the wood tree where we was cutting—he said, "I got to go."

"Go where?" I said.

"To that war," Pete said.

"Before we even finish gettin' in the firewood?"

"Firewood, hell," Pete said.

"All right," I said. "When we going to start?"

But he wasn't even listening. He laid there, hard and still as iron in the dark. "I got to go," he said. "I jest ain't going to put up with no folks treating the Unity States that way."

"Yes," I said. "Firewood or no firewood, I reckon we got to go."

This time he heard me. He laid still again, but it was a different kind of still.

"You?" he said. "To a war?"

"You'll whup the big uns and I'll whup the little uns," I said.

Then he told me I couldn't go. At first I thought he just never wanted me tagging after him, like he wouldn't leave me go with him when he went sparking them girls of Tull's. Then he told me the Army wouldn't leave me go because I was too little, and then I knowed he really meant it and that I couldn't go nohow noways. And somehow I hadn't believed until then that he was going himself, but now I knowed he was and that he wasn't going to leave me go with him a-tall.

"I'll chop the wood and tote the water for you-all then!" I said. "You got to have wood and water!"

Anyway, he was listening to me now. He wasn't like iron now.

He turned onto his side and put his hand on my chest because it was me that was laying straight and hard on my back now.

"No," he said. "You got to stay here and help pap."

"Help him what?" I said. "He ain't never caught up nohow. He can't get no further behind. He can sholy take care of this little shirttail of a farm while me and you are whupping them Japanese. I got to go too. If you got to go, then so have I."

"No," Pete said. "Hush now. Hush." And he meant it, and I knowed he did. Only I made sho from his own mouth. I quit.

"So I just can't go then," I said.

"No," Pete said. "You just can't go. You're too little, in the first place, and in the second place——"

"All right," I said. "Then shut up and leave me go to sleep."

So he hushed then and laid back. And I laid there like I was already asleep, and pretty soon he was asleep and I knowed it was the wanting to go to the war that had worried him and kept him awake, and now that he had decided to go, he wasn't worried any more.

The next morning he told maw and pap. Maw was all right. She cried.

"No," she said, crying, "I don't want him to go. I would rather go myself in his place, if I could. I don't want to save the country. Them Japanese could take it and keep it, so long as they left me and my family and my children alone. But I remember my brother Marsh in that other war. He had to go to that one when he wasn't but nineteen, and our mother couldn't understand it then any more than I can now. But she told Marsh if he had to go, he had to go. And so, if Pete's got to go to this one, he's got to go to it. Jest don't ask me to understand why."

But pap was the one. He was the feller. "To the war?" he said. "Why, I just don't see a bit of use in that. You ain't old enough for the draft, and the country ain't being invaded. Our President in Washington, D. C., is watching the conditions and he will notify us. Besides, in that other war your ma just mentioned, I was drafted and sent clean to Texas and was held there nigh eight months until they finally quit fighting. It seems to me that that, along with your Uncle Marsh who received a actual wound on the battlefields of France, is enough for me and mine to have to do to protect the country, at least in my lifetime. Besides, what'll I do for help on the farm with you gone? It seems to me I'll get mighty far behind."

"You been behind as long as I can remember," Pete said. "Anyway, I'm going. I got to."

"Of course he's got to go," I said. "Them Japanese——"

"You hush your mouth!" maw said, crying. "Nobody's talking to you! Go and get me a armful of wood! That's what you can do!"

So I got the wood. And all the next day, while me and Pete and pap was getting in as much wood as we could in that time because Pete said how pap's idea of plenty of wood was one more stick laying against the wall that maw ain't put on the fire yet, Maw was getting Pete ready to go. She washed and mended his clothes and cooked him a shoe box of vittles. And that night me and Pete laid in the bed and listened to her packing his grip and crying, until after a while Pete got up in his nightshirt and went back there, and I could hear them talking, until at last maw said, "You got to go, and so I want you to go. But I don't understand it, and I won't never, and so don't expect me to." And Pete come back and got into the bed again and laid again still and hard as iron on his back, and then he said, and he wasn't talking to me, he wasn't talking to nobody: "I got to go. I just got to."

"Sho you got to," I said. "Them Japanese——" He turned over hard, he kind of surged over onto his side, looking at me in the dark.

"Anyway, you're all right," he said. "I expected to have more trouble with you than with all the rest of them put together."

"I reckon I can't help it neither," I said. "But maybe it will run a few years longer and I can get there. Maybe someday I will jest walk in on you."

"I hope not," Pete said. "Folks don't go to wars for fun. A man don't leave his maw crying just for fun."

"Then why are you going?" I said.

"I got to," he said. "I just got to. Now you go on to sleep. I got to ketch that early bus in the morning."

"All right," I said. "I hear tell Memphis is a big place. How will you find where the Army's at?"

"I'll ask somebody where to go to join it," Pete said. "Go on to sleep now."

"Is that what you'll ask for? Where to join the Army?" I said.

"Yes," Pete said. He turned onto his back again. "Shut up and go to sleep."

We went to sleep. The next morning we et breakfast by lamplight because the bus would pass at six o'clock. Maw wasn't crying now. She jest looked grim and busy, putting breakfast on the table while we et it. Then she finished packing Pete's grip, except he never wanted to take no grip to the war, but maw said decent folks never went nowhere, not even to a war, without a change of clothes and something to tote them in. She put in the shoe box of fried chicken and biscuits and she put the Bible in, too, and then it was time to go. We didn't know until then that maw wasn't going to the bus. She jest brought Pete's cap and overcoat, and still she didn't cry no more, she jest stood with her hands on Pete's shoulders and she didn't move, but somehow, and just holding Pete's shoulders, she looked as hard and fierce as when Pete had turned toward me in the bed last night and tole me that anyway I was all right.

"They could take the country and keep the country, so long as they never bothered me and mine," she said. Then she said, "Don't never forget who you are. You ain't rich and the rest of the world outside of Frenchman's Bend never heard of you. But your blood is good as any blood anywhere, and don't you never forget it."

Then she kissed him, and then we was out of the house, with pap toting Pete's grip whether Pete wanted him to or not. There wasn't no dawn even yet, not even after we had stood on the highway by the mailbox, a while. Then we seen the lights of the bus coming and I was watching the bus until it come up and Pete flagged it, and then, sho enough, there was daylight—it had started while I wasn't watching. And now me and Pete expected pap to say something else foolish, like he done before, about how Uncle Marsh getting wounded in France and that trip to Texas pap taken in 1918 ought to be enough to save the Unity States in

1942, but he never. He done all right too. He jest said, "Good-by, son. Always remember what your ma told you and write her whenever you find the time." Then he shaken Pete's hand, and Pete looked at me a minute and put his hand on my head and rubbed my head durn nigh hard enough to wring my neck off and jumped into the bus, and the feller wound the door shut and the bus began to hum; then it was moving, humming and grinding and whining louder and louder; it was going fast, with two little red lights behind it that never seemed to get no littler, but just seemed to be running together until pretty soon they would touch and jest be one light. But they never did, and then the bus was gone, and even like it was, I could have pretty nigh busted out crying, nigh to nine years old and all.

Me and pap went back to the house. All that day we worked at the wood tree, and so I never had no good chance until about middle of the afternoon. Then I taken my slingshot and I would have liked to took all my bird eggs, too, because Pete had give me his collection and he holp me with mine, and he would like to git the box out and look at them as good as I would, even if he was nigh twenty years old. But the box was too big to tote a long ways and have to worry with, so I just taken the shikepoke egg, because it was the best un, and wropped it up good into a matchbox and hid it and the slingshot under the corner of the barn. Then we et supper and went to bed, and I thought then how if I would 'a' had to stayed in that room and that bed like that even for one more night, I jest couldn't 'a' stood it. Then I could hear pap snoring, but I never heard no sound from maw, whether she was asleep or not, and I don't reckon she was. So I taken my shoes and drapped them out the window, and then I clumb out like I used to watch Pete do when he was still jest seventeen and pap held that he was too young yet to be tom-catting around at night, and wouldn't leave him out, and I put on my shoes and went to the barn and got the slingshot and the shikepoke egg and went to the highway.

It wasn't cold, it was jest durn confounded dark, and that highway stretched on in front of me like, without nobody using

it, it had stretched out half again as fer just like a man does when
he lays down, so that for a time it looked like full sun was going
to ketch me before I had finished them twenty-two miles to
Jefferson. But it didn't. Daybreak was jest starting when I walked
up the hill into town. I could smell breakfast cooking in the cabins
and I wished I had thought to brought me a cold biscuit, but
that was too late now. And Pete had told me Memphis was a
piece beyond Jefferson, but I never knowed it was no eighty
miles. So I stood there on that empty square, with daylight
coming and coming and the street lights still burning and that
Law looking down at me, and me still eighty miles from Memphis, and it had took me all night to walk jest twenty-two miles,
and so, by the time I got to Memphis at that rate, Pete would 'a'
done already started for Pearl Harbor.

"Where do you come from?" the Law said.

And I told him again. "I got to get to Memphis. My brother's
there."

"You mean you ain't got any folks around here?" the Law
said. "Nobody but that brother? What are you doing way off
down here and your brother in Memphis?"

And I told him again, "I got to get to Memphis. I ain't got no
time to waste talking about it and I ain't got time to walk it. I got
to git there today."

"Come on here," the Law said.

We went down another street. And there was the bus, just
like when Pete got into it yestiddy morning, except there wasn't
no lights on it now and it was empty. There was a regular bus
dee-po like a railroad dee-po, with a ticket counter and a feller
behind it, and the Law said, "Set down over there," and I set
down on the bench, and the Law said, "I want to use your telephone," and he talked in the telephone a minute and put it down
and said to the feller behind the ticket counter, "Keep your eye
on him. I'll be back as soon as Mrs. Habersham can arrange to
get herself up and dressed." He went out. I got up and went to
the ticket counter.

"I want to go to Memphis," I said.

"You bet," the feller said. "You set down on the bench now. Mr. Foote will be back in a minute."

"I don't know no Mr. Foote," I said. "I want to ride that bus to Memphis."

"You got some money?" he said. "It'll cost you seventy-two cents."

I taken out the matchbox and unwropped the shikepoke egg. "I'll swap you this for a ticket to Memphis," I said.

"What's that?" he said.

"It's a shikepoke egg," I said. "You never seen one before. It's worth a dollar. I'll take seventy-two cents fer it."

"No," he said, "the fellers that own that bus insist on a cash basis. If I started swapping tickets for bird eggs and livestock and such, they would fire me. You go and set down on the bench now, like Mr. Foote——"

I started for the door, but he caught me, he put one hand on the ticket counter and jumped over it and caught up with me and reached his hand out to ketch my shirt. I whupped out my pocketknife and snapped it open.

"You put a hand on me and I'll cut it off," I said.

I tried to dodge him and run at the door, but he could move quicker than any grown man I ever see, quick as Pete almost. He cut me off and stood with his back against the door and one foot raised a little, and there wasn't no other way to get out. "Get back on that bench and stay there," he said.

And there wasn't no other way out. And he stood there with his back against the door. So I went back to the bench. And then it seemed like to me that dee-po was full of folks. There was that Law again, and there was two ladies in fur coats and their faces already painted. But they still looked like they had got up in a hurry and they still never liked it, a old one and a young one, looking down at me.

"He hasn't got a overcoat!" the old one said. "How in the world did he ever get down here by himself?"

"I ask you," the Law said. "I couldn't get nothing out of him except his brother is in Memphis and he wants to get back up there."

"That's right," I said. "I got to git to Memphis today."

"Of course you must," the old one said. "Are you sure you can find your brother when you get to Memphis?"

"I reckon I can," I said. "I ain't got but one and I have knowed him all my life. I reckon I will know him again when I see him."

The old one looked at me. "Somehow he doesn't look like he lives in Memphis," she said.

"He probably don't," the Law said. "You can't tell though. He might live anywhere, overhalls or not. This day and time they get scattered overnight from he—— hope to breakfast; boys and girls, too, almost before they can walk good. He might have been in Missouri or Texas either yestiddy, for all we know. But he don't seem to have any doubt his brother is in Memphis. All I know to do is send him up there and leave him look."

"Yes," the old one said.

The young one set down on the bench by me and opened a hand satchel and taken out a artermatic writing pen and some papers.

"Now, honey," the old one said, "we're going to see that you find your brother, but we must have a case history for our files first. We want to know your name and your brother's name and where you were born and when your parents died."

"I don't need no case history neither," I said. "All I want is to get to Memphis. I got to get there today."

"You see?" the Law said. He said it almost like he enjoyed it. "That's what I told you."

"You're lucky, at that, Mrs. Habersham," the bus feller said. "I don't think he's got a gun on him, but he can open that knife da—— I mean, fast enough to suit any man."

But the old one just stood there looking at me.

"Well," she said. "Well. I really don't know what to do."

"I do," the bus feller said. "I'm going to give him a ticket out of my own pocket, as a measure of protecting the company against riot and bloodshed. And when Mr. Foote tells the city board about it, it will be a civic matter and they will not only reimburse me, they will give me a medal too. Hey, Mr. Foote?"

But never nobody paid him no mind. The old one still stood looking down at me. She said "Well," again. Then she taken a dollar from her purse and give it to the bus feller. "I suppose he will travel on a child's ticket, won't he?"

"Wellum," the bus feller said, "I just don't know what the regulations would be. Likely I will be fired for not crating him and marking the crate Poison. But I'll risk it."

Then they were gone. Then the Law come back with a sandwich and give it to me.

"You're sure you can find that brother?" he said.

"I ain't yet convinced why not," I said. "If I don't see Pete first, he'll see me. He knows me too."

Then the Law went out for good, too, and I et the sandwich. Then more folks come in and bought tickets, and then the bus feller said it was time to go, and I got into the bus just like Pete done, and we was gone.

I seen all the towns. I seen all of them. When the bus got to going good, I found out I was jest about wore out for sleep. But there was too much I hadn't never saw before. We run out of Jefferson and run past fields and woods, then we would run into another town and out of that un and past fields and woods again, and then into another town with stores and gins and water tanks, and we run along by the railroad for a spell and I seen the signal arm move, and then I seen the train and then some more towns, and I was jest about plumb wore out for sleep, but I couldn't resk it. Then Memphis begun. It seemed like, to me, it went on for miles. We would pass a patch of stores and I would think that was sholy it and the bus would even stop. But it wouldn't be Memphis yet and we would go on again past water tanks and smokestacks on top of the mills, and if they was gins and saw-mills, I never knowed there was that many and I never seen any that big, and where they got enough cotton and logs to run um I don't know.

Then I see Memphis. I knowed I was right this time. It was standing up into the air. It looked like about a dozen whole towns bigger than Jefferson was set up on one edge in a field, standing up into the air higher than ara hill in all Yoknapatawpha County. Then we was in it, with the bus stopping ever' few feet, it seemed like to me, and cars rushing past on both sides of it and the street crowded with folks from ever'where in town that day, until I didn't see how there could 'a' been nobody left in Mis'sippi a-tall to even sell me a bus ticket, let alone write out no case histories. Then the bus stopped. It was another bus dee-po, a heap bigger than the one in Jefferson. And I said, "All right. Where do folks join the Army?"

"What?" the bus feller said.

And I said it again, "Where do folks join the Army?"

"Oh," he said. Then he told me how to get there. I was afraid at first I wouldn't ketch on how to do in a town big as Memphis. But I caught on all right. I never had to ask but twice more. Then I was there, and I was durn glad to git out of all them rushing cars and shoving folks and all that racket for a spell, and I thought, It won't be long now, and I thought how if there was any kind of a crowd there that had done already joined the Army, too, Pete would likely see me before I seen him. And so I walked into the room. And Pete wasn't there.

He wasn't even there. There was a soldier with a big arrer-head on his sleeve, writing, and two fellers standing in front of him, and there was some more folks there, I reckon. It seems to me I remember some more folks there.

I went to the table where the soldier was writing, and I said, "Where's Pete?" and he looked up and I said, "My brother. Pete Grier. Where is he?"

"What?" the soldier said. "Who?"

And I told him again. "He joined the Army yestiddy. He's going to Pearl Harbor. So am I. I want to ketch him. Where you all got him?" Now they were all looking at me, but I never paid them no mind. "Come on," I said. "Where is he?"

The soldier had quit writing. He had both hands spraddled out on the table. "Oh," he said. "You're going, too, hah?"

"Yes," I said. "They got to have wood and water. I can chop it and tote it. Come on. Where's Pete?"

The soldier stood up. "Who let you in here?" he said. "Go on. Beat it."

"Durn that," I said. "You tell me where Pete——"

I be dog if he couldn't move faster than the bus feller even. He never come over the table, he come around it, he was on me almost before I knowed it, so that I jest had time to jump back and whup out my pocket-knife and snap it open and hit one lick, and he hollered and jumped back and grabbed one hand with the other and stood there cussing and hollering.

One of the other fellers grabbed me from behind, and I hit at him with the knife, but I couldn't reach him.

Then both of the fellers had me from behind, and then another soldier come out of a door at the back. He had on a belt with a britching strop over one shoulder.

"What the hell is this?" he said.

"That little son cut me with a knife!" the first soldier hollered. When he said that I tried to get at him again, but both them fellers was holding me, two against one, and the soldier with the backing strop said, "Here, here. Put your knife up, feller. None of us are armed. A man don't knife-fight folks that are barehanded." I could begin to hear him then. He sounded jest like Pete talked to me. "Let him go," he said. They let me go. "Now what's all the trouble about?" And I told him. "I see," he said. "And you come up to see if he was all right before he left."

"No," I said. "I came to——"

But he had already turned to where the first soldier was wropping a handkerchief around his hand.

"Have you got him?" he said. The first soldier went back to the table and looked at some papers.

"Here he is," he said. "He enlisted yestiddy. He's in a detach-

ment leaving this morning for Little Rock." He had a watch
stropped on his arm. He looked at it. "The train leaves in about
fifty minutes. If I know country boys, they're probably all down
there at the station now."

"Get him up here," the one with the backing strop said.
"Phone the station. Tell the porter to get him a cab. And you
come with me," he said.

It was another office behind that un, with jest a table and
some chairs. We set there while the soldier smoked, and it wasn't
long; I knowed Pete's feet soon as I heard them. Then the first
soldier opened the door and Pete come in. He never had no
soldier clothes on. He looked jest like he did when he got on the
bus yestiddy morning, except it seemed to me like it was at least
a week, so much had happened, and I had done had to do so
much traveling. He come in and there he was, looking at me like
he hadn't never left home, except that here we was in Memphis,
on the way to Pearl Harbor.

"What in durnation are you doing here?" he said.

And I told him, "You got to have wood and water to cook
with. I can chop it and tote it for you-all."

"No," Pete said. "You're going back home."

"No, Pete," I said. "I got to go too. I got to. It hurts my
heart, Pete."

"No," Pete said. He looked at the soldier. "I jest don't know
what could have happened to him, lootenant," he said. "He never
drawed a knife on anybody before in his life." He looked at me.
"What did you do it for?"

"I don't know," I said. "I jest had to. I jest had to git here.
I jest had to find you."

"Well, don't you never do it again, you hear?" Pete said.
"You put that knife in your pocket and you keep it there. If I
ever again hear of you drawing it on anybody, I'm coming back
from wherever I am at and whup the fire out you. You hear me?"

"I would pure cut a throat if it would bring you back to
stay," I said. "Pete," I said. "Pete."

"No," Pete said. Now his voice wasn't hard and quick no

more, it was almost quiet, and I knowed now I wouldn't never change him. "You must go home. You must look after maw, and I am depending on you to look after my ten acres. I want you to go back home. Today. Do you hear?"

"I hear," I said.

"Can he get back home by himself?" the soldier said.

"He come up here by himself," Pete said.

"I can get back, I reckon," I said. "I don't live in but one place. I don't reckon it's moved."

Pete taken a dollar out of his pocket and give it to me. "That'll buy your bus ticket right to our mailbox," he said. "I want you to mind the lootenant. He'll send you to the bus. And you go back home and you take care of maw and look after my ten acres and keep that durn knife in your pocket. You hear me?"

"Yes, Pete," I said.

"All right," Pete said. "Now I got to go." He put his hand on my head again. But this time he never wrung my neck. He just laid his hand on my head a minute. And then I be dog if he didn't lean down and kiss me, and I heard his feet and then the door, and I never looked up and that was all, me setting there, rubbing the place where Pete kissed me and the soldier throwed back in his chair, looking out the window and coughing. He reached into his pocket and handed something to me without looking around. It was a piece of chewing gum.

"Much obliged," I said. "Well, I reckon I might as well start back. I got a right fer piece to go."

"Wait," the soldier said. Then he telephoned again and I said again I better start back, and he said again, "Wait. Remember what Pete told you."

So we waited, and then another lady come in, old, too, in a fur coat, too, but she smelled all right, she never had no arter-matic writing pen nor no case history neither. She come in and the soldier got up, and she looked around quick until she saw me, and come and put her hand on my shoulder light and quick and easy as maw herself might 'a' done it.

"Come on," she said. "Let's go home to dinner."

"Nome," I said. "I got to ketch the bus to Jefferson."

"I know. There's plenty of time. We'll go home and eat dinner first."

She had a car. And now we was right down in the middle of all them other cars. We was almost under the busses, and all them crowds of people on the street close enough to where I could have talked to them if I had knowed who they was. After a while she stopped the car. "Here we are," she said, and I looked at it, and if all that was her house, she sho had a big family. But all of it wasn't. We crossed a hall with trees growing in it and went into a little room without nothing in it but a nigger dressed up in a uniform a heap shinier than them soldiers had, and the nigger shut the door, and then I hollered, "Look out!" and grabbed, but it was all right; that whole little room just went right on up and stopped and the door opened and we was in another hall, and the lady unlocked a door and we went in, and there was another soldier, a old feller, with a britching strop, too, and a silver-colored bird on each shoulder.

"Here we are," the lady said. "This is Colonel McKellogg. Now, what would you like for dinner?"

"I reckon I'll jest have some ham and eggs and coffee," I said.

She had done started to pick up the telephone. She stopped. "Coffee?" she said. "When did you start drinking coffee?"

"I don't know," I said. "I reckon it was before I could remember."

"You're about eight, aren't you?" she said.

"Nome," I said. "I'm eight and ten months. Going on eleven months."

She telephoned then. Then we set there and I told them how Pete had jest left that morning for Pearl Harbor and I had aimed to go with him, but I would have to go back home to take care of maw and look after Pete's ten acres, and she said how they had a little boy about my size, too, in a school in the East. Then a nigger, another one, in a short kind of shirttail coat, rolled a kind of wheelbarrer in. It had my ham and eggs and a glass of milk and a piece of pie, too, and I thought I was hungry. But when I taken the first bite I found out I couldn't swallow it, and I got up quick.

"I got to go," I said.

"Wait," she said.

"I got to go," I said.

"Just a minute," she said. "I've already telephoned for the car. It won't be but a minute now. Can't you drink the milk even? Or maybe some of your coffee?"

"Nome," I said. "I ain't hungry. I'll eat when I git home." Then the telephone rung. She never even answered it.

"There," she said. "There's the car." And we went back down in that 'ere little moving room with the dressed-up nigger. This time it was a big car with a soldier driving it. I got in front with him. She give the soldier a dollar. "He might get hungry," she said. "Try to find a decent place for him."

"O.K., Mrs. McKellogg," the soldier said.

Then we was gone again. And now I could see Memphis good, bright in the sunshine, while we was swinging around it. And first thing I knowed, we was back on the same highway the bus run on this morning—the patches of stores and them big gins and sawmills, and Memphis running on for miles, it seemed like to me, before it begun to give out. Then we was running again between the fields and woods, running fast now, and except for that soldier, it was like I hadn't never been to Memphis a-tall. We was going fast now. At this rate, before I knowed it we would be home again, and I thought about me riding up to Frenchman's Bend in this big car with a soldier running it, and all of a sudden I begun to cry. I never knowed I was fixing to, and I couldn't stop it. I set there by that soldier, crying. We was going fast.

BUDD SCHULBERG

My Christmas Carol

When I was a little boy, I lived with my parents in what was then a small suburb of Los Angeles called Hollywood. My father was general manager in charge of production for Firmament-Famous Artists-Lewin. It was a mouthful, but I used to have to remember the whole thing for the your-father-my-father arguments I was always having with a kid down the block whose old man was only an associate producer at Warner Brothers.

One of the things I remember most about Firmament-Famous Artists-Lewin was the way that studio and Christmas were all mixed up together in my mind. My earliest memory of the Christmas season is associated with a large studio truck, bearing the company's trademark, that always drove up to the house just before supper on Christmas Eve. I would stand outside the kitchen door with my little sister and watch the driver and his helper carry into our house armload after armload of wonderful red and green packages—all for us. Sometimes the gleaming handlebars of a tricycle or the shiny wheels of a miniature fire engine would break through their bright wrappers, and I'd shout, "I know what that is!" until my mother would lead me away. Santa Claus still had so many houses to visit, she'd say, that I mustn't get in the way of these two helpers of his. Then I'd go down the street to argue the respective merits of our two studios with the Warner Brothers kid, or pass the time tormenting my little sister, perfectly content in the thought that the Firmament-Famous Artists-Lewin truck was the standard vehicle of transportation for Santa Claus in semitropical climates like Southern California.

On Christmas morning I had the unfortunate habit of rising at five o'clock, rushing across the hallway to my sister's room in annual disobedience of my mother's request to rise quietly, and shouting, "Merry Christmas, Sandra! Let's wake Mommy and Daddy and open our presents."

We ran down the hall into the master bedroom with its canopied twin beds. "Merry Christmas!" we shouted together. My father groaned, rolled over and pulled the covers further up over his head. He was suffering the after-effects of the studio's annual all-day Christmas party from which he hadn't returned until after we had gone to sleep. I climbed up on the bed, crawling over him, and bounced up and down, chanting, "Merry Christmas, Merry Christmas. . . ."

"Oh-h-h . . ." Father said, and flipped over on his belly. Mother shook his shoulder gently. "Sol, I hate to wake you, but the children won't go down without you."

Father sat up slowly, muttering something about its being still dark outside and demanding to know who had taken his bathrobe. Mother picked it up where he had dropped it and brought it to him. It was black and white silk with an elegant embroidered monogram.

"The kids'll be opening presents for the next twelve hours," my father said. "It seems God-damn silly to start opening them at five o'clock in the morning."

Downstairs there were enough toys, it seemed, to fill all the windows of a department store. The red car was a perfect model of a Pierce-Arrow, and probably only slightly less expensive, with a green leather seat wide enough for Sandra to sit beside me, and real headlights that turned on and off. There was a German electric train that passed through an elaborate Bavarian village in miniature. And a big scooter with rubber wheels and a gear shift just like our Cadillac's. And dozens more that I've forgotten. Sandra had a doll that was a life-size replica of Baby Peggy, which was Early Twenties for Margaret O'Brien, an imported silk Hungarian peasant costume from Lord & Taylor, a six-ounce bottle of French toilet water, and so many other things that we all had to help her unwrap them.

Just when we were reaching the end of this supply, people started arriving with more presents. That's the way it had been every Christmas since I could remember, men and women all dressed up dropping in all day long with packages containing wonderful things that they'd wait for us to unwrap. They'd sit around a while, laughing with my mother and father and lifting from James the butler's tray a cold yellow drink that I wasn't allowed to have, and then they'd pick us up and kiss us and tell us we were as pretty as my mother or as intelligent as my father and then there would be more laughing and hugging and hand-shaking and God bless you and then they'd be gone, and others would arrive to take their place. Sometimes there must have been ten or twenty all there at once and Sandra and I would be sort of sorry in a way because Mother and Father would be too busy with their guests to play with us. But it was nice to get all those presents.

I remember one tall dark man with a little pointed mustache who kissed Mother's hand when he came in. His present was wrapped in beautiful silvery paper and the blue ribbon around it felt thick and soft like one of Mother's evening dresses. Inside was a second layer of thin white tissue paper and inside of that was a handsome silver comb-and-brush set, just like my father's. Tied to it was a little card that I could read because it was printed and I could read almost anything then as long as it wasn't hand-writing: "Merry Christmas to my future boss from Uncle Norman."

"Mommy," I said, "is Uncle Norman my uncle? You never told me I had an Uncle Norman. I have an Uncle Dave and an

Uncle Joe and an Uncle Sam, but I never knew I had an Uncle Norman."

I can still remember how white and even Norman's teeth looked when he smiled at me. "I'm a new uncle," he said. "Don't you remember the day your daddy brought you on my set and I signed your autograph book and I told you to call me Uncle Norman?"

I combed my hair with his silver comb suspiciously. "Did you give me this comb and brush . . . Uncle Norman?"

Norman drank down the last of the foamy yellow stuff and carefully wiped off his mustache with his pale-blue breast-pocket handkerchief. "Yes, I did sonny," he said.

I turned on my mother accusingly. "But you said Santa Claus gives us all these presents."

This all took place as I found out later, at a crucial moment in my relationship with S. Claus, when a child's faith was beginning to crumble under the pressure of suspicions. Mother was trying to keep Santa Claus alive for us as long as possible, I learned subsequently, so that Christmas would mean something more to us than a display of sycophancy on the part of Father's stars, directors, writers and job-seekers.

"Norman signed his name to your comb and brush because he is one of Santa Claus's helpers," Mother said. "Santa has so much work to do taking care of all the good little children in the world that he needs lots and lots of helpers."

My father offered one of his long, fat cigars to "Uncle" Norman and bit off the end of another one for himself.

"Daddy, is that true, what Mommy says?" I asked.

"You must always believe your mother, boy," my father said.

"I've got twenty-eleven presents already," Sandra said.

"You mean thirty-one," I said. "I've got thirty-two."

Sandra tore open a box that held an exquisite little gold ring, inlaid with amethyst, her birthstone.

"Let me read the card," I said. "'Merry Christmas, Sandra darling, from your biggest fan, Aunt Ruth.'"

Ruth was the pretty lady who played opposite Uncle Norman in one of my father's recent pictures. I hadn't been allowed to see it, but I used to boast to that Warner Brothers kid about how much better it was than anything Warners' could make. Sandra, being very young, tossed Aunt Ruth's gold ring away and turned slowly in her hand the little box it had come in. "Look, it says numbers on it," she said. "Why are the numbers, Chris?"

I studied it carefully. "Ninety-five. That looks like dollars," I said. "Ninety-five dollars. Where does Santa Claus get all his money, Daddy?"

My father gave my mother a questioning look. "Er . . . what's that, son?" I had to repeat the question. "Oh . . . those aren't dollars, no . . . That's just the number Santa puts on his toys to keep them from getting all mixed up before he sends them down from the North Pole," my father said, and then he took a deep breath and another gulp of that yellow drink.

More people kept coming in all afternoon. More presents. More uncles and aunts. More Santa Claus's helpers. I never realized he had so many helpers. All afternoon the phone kept ringing, too. "Sol, you might as well answer it, it must be for you," my mother would say, and then I could hear my father laughing on the phone: "Thanks, L.B., and a Merry Christmas to you . . . Thanks, Joe . . . Thanks, Mary . . . Thanks, Doug . . . Merry Christmas, Pola . . ." Gifts kept arriving late into the day, sometimes in big limousines and town cars, carried in by chauffeurs in snappy uniforms. No matter how my father explained it, it seemed to me that Santa must be as rich as Mr. Zukor.

Just before supper, one of the biggest stars in Father's pictures drove up in a Rolls Royce roadster, the first one I had ever seen. She came in with a tall, broad-shouldered, sunburned man who laughed at anything anybody said. She was a very small lady and she wore her hair tight around her head like a boy's. She had on a tight yellow dress that only came down to the top of her knees. She and the man she was with had three presents for me and four for Sandra. She looked down at me and said, "Merry Christmas, you little darling," and before I could get away, she picked me up and was kissing me. She smelled all funny, with perfumy sweetness mixed up with the way Father smelled when he came home from that Christmas party at the studio and leaned over my bed to kiss me when I was half asleep.

I didn't like people to kiss me, especially strangers. "Lemme go," I said.

"That's no way to act, Sonny," the strange man said. "Why, right this minute every man in America would like to be in your shoes."

All the grownups laughed, but I kept squirming, trying to get away. "Aw, don't be that way, honey," the movie star said. "Why, I love men!"

They all laughed again. I didn't understand it so I started to cry. Then she put me down. "All right for you," she said, "if you don't want to be my boy friend."

After she left, when I was unwrapping her presents, I asked my father, "Who is she? Is she one of Santa Claus's helpers, too?" Father winked at Mother, turned his head away, put his hand to his mouth and laughed into it, but I saw him. Mother looked at him the way she did when she caught me taking a piece of candy just before supper. "Her name is Clara, dear," she said. "She's one of Santa Claus's helpers, too."

And that's the way Christmas was, until one Christmas when a funny thing happened. The big Firmament-Famous Artists-Lewin truck never showed up. I kept looking for it all afternoon, but it never came. When it got dark and it was time for me to have my supper and go to bed and still no truck, I got pretty worried. My mind ran back through the year trying to remember some bad thing I might have done that Santa was going to punish me for. I had done lots of bad things, like slapping my sister and breaking my father's fountain pen, but they were no worse than the stuff I had pulled the year before. Yet what other reason could there possibly be for that truck not showing up?

Another thing that seemed funny about that Christmas Eve was that my father didn't bother to go to his studio Christmas party. He stayed home all morning and read aloud to me from a Christmas present he let me open a day early, a big blue book called *Typee*. And late that night when I tiptoed halfway down the stairs to watch my mother trim the tree that Santa was supposed to decorate, my father was helping her string the colored lights. Another thing different about Christmas was that when Sandra and I ran in shouting and laughing at five, as we always did, my father got up as soon as my mother.

When we went downstairs, we found almost as many presents as on other Christmas mornings. There was a nice fire engine from Uncle Norman, a cowboy suit from Aunt Ruth, a Meccano set from Uncle Adolph, something, in fact, from every one of Santa Claus's helpers. No, it wasn't the presents that made this Christmas seem so different, it was how quiet every thing was. Pierce-Arrows and Packards and Cadillacs didn't keep stopping by all day long with new presents for us. And none of the people like Norman and Ruth and Uncle Edgar, the famous director, and Aunt Betty, the rising ingenue, and Uncle Dick, the young star, and the scenario writer, Uncle Bill, none of them dropped in at all. James the butler was gone, too. For the first Christmas since I could remember, we had father all to ourselves. Even the phone was quiet for a change. Except for a couple of real relatives, the only one who showed up at all was Clara. She came in around supper time with an old man whose hair was yellow at the temples and gray on top. Her face was very red and when she picked me up to kiss me, her breath reminded me of the Christmas before, only stronger. My father poured her and her friend the foamy yellow drink I wasn't allowed to have.

She held up her drink and said, "Merry Christmas, Sol. And may next Christmas be even merrier."

My father's voice sounded kind of funny, not laughing as he usually did. "Thanks, Clara," he said. "You're a pal."

"Nerts," Clara said. "Just because I don't wanna be a fair-weather friend like some of these other Hollywood bas—"

"Shhh, the children," my mother reminded her.

"Oh hell, I'm sorry," Clara said. "But anyway, you know what I mean."

My mother looked from us to Clara and back to us again. "Chris, Sandra," she said. "Why don't you take your toys up to your own room and play? We'll be up later."

In three trips I carried up to my room all the important presents. I also took up a box full of cards that had been attached to the presents. As a bit of holiday homework, our penmanship teacher Miss Whitehead had suggested that we separate all Christmas-card signatures into those of Spencerian grace and those of cramp-fingered illegibility. I played with my Meccano set for a while, I practiced twirling my lasso and I made believe Sandra was an Indian, captured her and tied her to the bedstead as my hero Art Acord did in the movies. I captured Sandra three or four times and then I didn't know what to do with myself, so I spread all the Christmas cards out on the floor and began sorting them just as Miss Whitehead had asked.

I sorted half a dozen, all quite definitely non-Spencerian, but it wasn't until I had sorted ten or twelve that I began to notice something funny. It was all the same handwriting. Then I came to a card of my father's. I was just beginning to learn how to read handwriting, and I wasn't very good at it yet, but I could recognize the three little bunched-together letters that spelled *Dad*. I held my father's card close to my eyes and compared it with the one from Uncle Norman. It was the same handwriting. Then I compared them with the one from Uncle Adolph. All the same handwriting. Then I picked up one of Sandra's cards, from Aunt Ruth, and held that one up against my father's. I couldn't understand it. My father seemed to have written them all.

I didn't say anything to Sandra about this, or to the nurse when she gave us our supper and put us to bed. But when my mother came in to kiss me good night, I asked her why my father's handwriting was on all the cards. My mother turned on the light and sat on the edge of the bed.

"You don't really believe in Santa Claus any more, do you?" she asked.

"No," I said. "Fred and Clyde told me all about it at school."

"Then I don't think it will hurt you to know the rest," my mother said. "Sooner or later you will have to know these things." Then she told me what had happened. Between last Christmas and this one, my father had lost his job. He was trying to start his own company now. Lots of stars and directors had promised to go with him. But when the time had come to make good on their promises, they had backed out. Though I didn't fully understand it at the time, even in the simplified way my mother tried to explain it, I would say now that for most of those people the security of a major-company payroll had outweighed an adventure on Poverty Row—the name for the group of little studios where the independent producers struggled to survive.

So this had been a lean year for my father. We had sold one of the cars, let the butler go, and lived on a budget. As Christmas approached, Mother had cut our presents to a minimum.

"Anyway, the children will be taken care of," my father said. "The old gang will see to that."

The afternoon of Christmas Eve my father had had a business appointment, to see a banker about more financing for his program of pictures. When he came home, Sandra and I had just gone to bed, and Mother was arranging the presents around the tree. There weren't many presents to arrange, just a few they themselves had bought. There were no presents at all from my so-called aunts and uncles.

"My pals," Father said. "My admirers. My loyal employees."

Even though he had the intelligence to understand why these people had always sent us those expensive presents, his vanity, or perhaps I can call it his good nature, had led him to believe they did it because they liked him and because they genuinely were fond of Sandra and me.

"I'm afraid the kids will wonder what happened to all those Santa Claus's helpers," my mother said.

"Wait a minute," my father said. "I've got an idea. Those

bastards are going to be Santa Claus's helpers whether they know it or not."

Then he had rushed out to a toy store on Hollywood Boulevard and bought a gift for every one of the aunts and uncles who were so conspicuously absent.

I remember, when my mother finished explaining, how I bawled. I don't know whether it was out of belated gratitude to my old man or whether I was feeling sorry for myself because all those famous people didn't like me as much as I thought they did. Maybe I was only crying because that first, wonderful and ridiculous part of childhood was over. From now on I would have to face a world in which there was not only no Santa Claus, but very, very few on-the-level Santa Claus's helpers.

P. B. HUGHES

Catherine and the Winter Wheat

This is the winter wheat that is being hauled along the roads in late July or early August in southern Ontario, the winter wheat, the fall wheat—have it how you will.

It is sown in September, about the time of the equinox, when the wind blows northwesterly, or used to, across Star-of-the-Sea, and the heavy rain has not come. It stands through the winter, withering under the snow like common grass, blazing emerald in spring, and by early June it is breast-high, fading in color and heading up, as the farmers say, looking to their binders against July, when the field will be yellow gold and heavy with grain.

It was our sole cash crop, and the brief season when we hauled wheat to the mill was always associated with new clothes and toys and coins in our pockets when my sisters and I were children.

One year before the war we carried our wheat, as we always did, to the mill at Streetsville on the Credit River. I was in my first teens. Before the war, the 1914 war, long ago now. I rode on the sacks, sitting beside my sister Catherine, who was sixteen now, or nearly, while my father drove the team and Emily, the oldest of us, seventeen, sat beside him and spelled him with the reins.

That way the trip took hours, though you'd cover it in a few minutes today in a car. But the sun was bright and the day fresh and beautiful after all the rain and the humid heat of the summer, and I talked away to Catherine and thought of the delight to come, of lying under the trees at the miller's while we waited our turn to unload and my father chatted with the men and smoked his pipe, and the greatest delight of all, when the wagon was empty and my father would give us money and tell us to get about our shopping.

Catherine paid no attention to what I said. Dark and stormy she sat on the jolting wagon, for all the glory of this most glorious day.

She had the letter shoved into her blouse, the letter she'd written the night before when everyone was in bed, a secret portentous letter, probably misspelled, but still one of those papers which shape the history of the world.

Oh, I heard the lamp being lit and saw the shadowy figure scratching away, and I knew all about her and Tom Skaife, and what would be in the letter, so I went to sleep again. Skaife's was only a mile out of Streetsville. For certain I'd be dispatched to deliver it personally and privately to Tom before we all set out home again, and Tom would be along one night to get her, and the two of them off to be married at Hamilton, where Tom worked at the iron works except in the harvest season.

That's the way it was, and the reason Catherine's singing was muted that summer and she so fiery and quick to take the corn broom to a boy that got in her way about the place. There wasn't anything against Tom. It was just a matter of their both being so young, and the two years of waiting demanded of them so intolerably too much. Catherine and I were close to one another, and I think I could tell what she was thinking. That is how I knew what was in the letter. I never saw it.

So Catherine brooded on the top of the rumbling wagonload, and I grieved beside her that I was to lose her, but I was a lad brought up on the land and aware already that all life was ordered in awful cycles of growth and generation and decay, and go she must, soon or late. And today there would be the long ride in the sun, which was far-travel to me, the stream of grain as the sacks were emptied, and money rattling in my pocket, and I could not keep on with grieving and regretting when I contemplated these things.

This summer, this trip to the Credit River, this harvest, are special in my memory. There was Catherine and Tom Skaife. Then there was the wetness of the July and the heat. The two factors got strangely mixed up during the course of the day, which is a trick Nature is playing all the time while she is weaving away at the destinies of men. My father, unaware of this letter writing, was unusually preoccupied, worrying about the condition of the wheat he carried, for grain is sensitive to the weather in which it has matured and been harvested.

We knew that a good deal of wheat had been turned away at the mill in the last week for toughness, which is a matter of moisture content and difficult to deal with, though they do have drying equipment now at the mills which takes care of a lot of doubtful stuff. You daren't bin it though. Heating and spoilage is an ever-present risk.

At that time you hauled it home again, and you might dry it out with untold labor by spreading it out on the floor in the threshold of the barn, and keep it or sell it degraded for feed. Then, too, your barn was stuffed with hay and with straw from the threshing so you hadn't any floor to spread it on.

My father pondered the matter as he drove, and Emily, sensitive to the moods of others, was quiet. Catherine was wrapped in her own thoughts. Only I was possessed of the high spirits proper to the occasion.

There wasn't much waiting around at the mill. Some years all the farmers seemed to arrive together and you might be four or five hours in line, and other times the season was strung out so you could get a load in when you brought it. We all went into the miller's office together. Old Mr. Jonathan remembered all our names, inquired for my mother, and complained of his rheumatism, the hard times, the cost of labor, the sad wheat he'd been

brought and how much he'd had to refuse. It was the same each
year, but this year it was the toughness of the wheat he grumbled
about most.

"Well, William," he said at last, "dump her off. No need to
sample Laughlin's wheat, anyway."

The girls and I looked at each other with relief. I felt like
jumping up and down, for there is no doubt the worry about
selling the wheat had been urgent in the last hour. My father and
his father, the old Laughlin who bought Star-of-the-Sea from the
O'Rourkes who built it in '69, were staunch men, and men of
substance, but the substance was seldom cash.

My father stood there quite still, and the rest of us, starting
for the door of the office, halted when he did not turn to go.

"No, Jonathan," he said, after a little pause, "I guess we'd
better sample this. It's not been a good summer."

The miller got up, a little surprised.

"H'm. All right. Thought it mightn't have been so bad your
way."

They went out together, and we followed without speaking
to each other, and my father and the miller opened a lot of sacks,
and talked as they pushed their hands into the wheat. Then they
carried a couple of sample tins into the office and remained there
for what seemed hours to us. At last my father came out and
when we saw his face, our hearts sank. He didn't say anything but
climbed back onto the wagon, and we got up beside him and
around behind him, and he worked the wagon around and we
started back toward the road.

At the road, he swung the team down toward the town and
halted under the trees in front of the post office. Then he pulled
a dollar out of his pocket and told Emily to get something for her
mother and some ice cream for us while the horses were rested
and watered.

But we didn't move at once. The blow had been heavy. I
thought: Catherine is going to give me that letter to take to Tom
while Father is seeing to the horses. Then suddenly there were

tears in Emily's eyes and she turned on my father, hurt and passionate.

"Oh, why couldn't you have unloaded the wheat when he told you to? Why haven't you got the money for it? What did you say it had to be tested for?"

My father looked at her and at us. Three pairs of eyes were upon him, wide-open, puzzled, accusing, in that moment or two before he spoke. Actually he said very little by way of answer. Only, "Children, you'd better remember this all your lives."

I think we must have stared at him a long time before we turned away, ashamed, realizing the enormity of what had been in our minds, of what Emily had expressed. We got down slowly off the wheat, leaving Father, and went into the shop and ate ice-cream cones, not talking and not looking at each other.

Suddenly Catherine pulled out the letter and tore it across and across, again and again, until it was only small wads of paper too thick to tear. She pushed the bits into her pocket and ran out without a word, her face wet with tears, to where my father was tending the horses.

Emily and I went and got some bit of something for Mother, and eventually we all got back on the wagon and went home with the sun setting in front of us, and that is all there was to that day—but I have remembered.

CONRAD AIKEN

Impulse

Michael Lowes hummed as he shaved, amused by the face he saw, the pallid, asymmetrical face, with the right eye so much higher than the left, and its eyebrow so peculiarly arched, like a "v" turned upside down. Perhaps this day wouldn't be as bad as the last. In fact, he knew it wouldn't be, and that was why he hummed. This was the bi-weekly day of escape, when he would stay out for the evening, and play bridge with Hurwitz, Bryant, and Smith. Should he tell Dora at the breakfast table? No, better not. Particularly in view of last night's row about unpaid bills. And there would be more of them, probably, beside his plate. The rent. The coal. The doctor who had attended to the children. Jeez, what a life. Maybe it was a time to do a new jump. And Dora was beginning to get restless again—.

But he hummed, thinking of the bridge-game. Not that he liked Hurwitz or Bryant or Smith—cheap fellows, really—mere pick-up acquaintances. But what could you do about making friends, when you were always hopping about from one place to another, looking for a living, and fate always against you! They were all right enough. Good enough for a little escape, a little party,—and Hurwitz always provided good alcohol. Dinner at the Greek's, and then to Smith's room—yes. He would wait till late in the afternoon, and then telephone to Dora as if it had all come up suddenly. Hello Dora—is that you, old girl? Yes, this is

Michael—Smith has asked me to drop in for a hand of bridge—you know—so I'll just have a little snack in town. Home by the last car as usual. Yes. . . . Gooo-by! . . .

And it all went off perfectly, too. Dora was quiet, at breakfast, but not hostile. The pile of bills was there, to be sure, but nothing was said about them. And while Dora was busy getting the kids ready for school, he managed to slip out, pretending that he thought it was later than it really was. Pretty neat, that! He hummed again, as he waited for the train. Telooralooraloo. Let the bills wait, damn them! A man couldn't do everything at once, could he, when bad luck hounded him everywhere? And if he could just get a little night off, now and then, a rest and change, a little diversion, what was the harm in that?

At half-past four he rang up Dora and broke the news to her. He wouldn't be home till late.

"Are you sure you'll be home at all?" she said, coolly.

That was Dora's idea of a joke. But if he could have foreseen—!

He met the others at the Greek restaurant, began with a couple of *araks*, which warmed him, then went on to red wine, bad olives, *pilaf*, and other obscure foods; and considerably later they all walked along Boylston Street to Smith's room. It was a cold night, the temperature below twenty, with a fine dry snow sifting the streets. But Smith's room was comfortably warm, he trotted out some gin and the Porto Rican cigars, showed them a new snapshot of Squiggles (his Revere Beach sweetheart), and then they settled down to a nice long cosy game of bridge.

It was during an intermission, when they all got up to stretch their legs and renew their drinks, that the talk started—Michael never could remember which one of them it was who had put in the first oar—about impulse. It might have been Hurwitz, who was in many ways the only intellectual one of the three, though hardly what you might call a highbrow. He had his queer curiosities, however, and the idea was just such as might occur to him. At any rate, it was he who developed the idea, and with gusto.

"Sure," he said, "anybody might do it. Have you got im-

pulses? Of course you got impulses. How many times you think
—suppose I do that? And you don't do it, because you know
damn well if you do it you'll get arrested. You meet a man you
despise—you want to spit in his eye. You see a girl you'd like to
kiss—you want to kiss her. Or maybe just to squeeze her arm
when she stands beside you in the street-car. You know what I
mean."

"DO I know what you *mean!*" sighed Smith. "I'll tell the
world. I'll tell the cock-eyed world! . . ."

"You would," said Bryant. "And so would I."

"It would be easy," said Hurwitz, "to give in to it. You know
what I mean? So simple. Temptation is too close. That girl you
see is too damn good-looking—she stands too near you—you just
put out your hand it touches her arm,—maybe her leg,—why
worry? And you think, maybe if she don't like it I can make
believe I didn't mean it. . . ."

"Like these fellows that slash fur coats with razor-blades,"
said Michael. "Just impulse, in the beginning, and only later a
habit."

"Sure. . . . And like these fellows that cut off braids of hair
with scissors. They just feel like it and do it. . . . Or stealing."

"Stealing?" said Bryant.

"Sure. Why, I often feel like it. . . . I see a nice little thing
right in front of me on a counter—you know, a nice little knife,
or necktie, or a box of candy—quick, you put it in your pocket,
and then go to the other counter, or the soda fountain for a drink.
What would be more human? We all want things. Why not take
them? Why not do them? And civilization is only skin deep. . . ."

"That's right. Skin deep," said Bryant.

"But if you were caught, by God!" said Smith, opening his
eyes wide.

"*Who's* talking about getting caught? . . . *Who's* talking
about doing it? It isn't that we do it, it's only that we *want* to
do it. Why, Christ, there's been times when I thought to hell
with everything. I'll kiss that woman if it's the last thing I do."

"It might be," said Bryant.

Michael was astonished at this turn of the talk. He had often felt both these impulses. To know that this was a kind of universal human inclination came over him with something like relief. "Of *course* everybody has those feelings," he said, smiling. "I have them myself. . . . But suppose you *did* yield to them?" "Well, we don't," said Hurwitz. "I know,—but suppose you did?" Hurwitz shrugged his fat shoulders, indifferently. "Oh well," he said, "it would be bad business." "Jesus, yes," said Smith, shuffling the cards. "Oy," said Bryant.

The game was resumed, the glasses were re-filled, pipes were lit, watches were looked at. Michael had to think of the last car from Sullivan Square, at eleven-fifty. But also he could not stop thinking of this strange idea. It was amusing. It was fascinating. Here was everyone wanting to steal—tooth brushes, or books— or to caress some fascinating stranger of a female in a subway train—the impulse everywhere—why not be a Columbus of the moral world and really do it? . . . He remembered stealing a conch-shell from the drawing-room of a neighbor when he was ten—it had been one of the thrills of his life. He had popped it into his sailor-blouse and borne it away with perfect aplomb. When, later, suspicion had been cast upon him, he had smashed the shell in his back yard. And often, when he had been looking at Parker's collection of stamps—the early Americans—

The game interrupted his recollections, and presently it was time for the usual night-cap. Bryant drove them to Park Street. Michael was a trifle tight, but not enough to be unsteady on his feet. He waved a cheery hand at Bryant and Hurwitz and began to trudge through the snow to the subway entrance. The lights on the snow were very beautiful. The Park Street Church was ringing, with its queer, soft quarter-bells, the half hour. Plenty of time. Plenty of time. Time enough for a visit to the drug-store, and a hot chocolate—he could see the warm lights of the windows falling on the snowed sidewalk. He zigzagged across the street and entered.

And at once he was seized with a conviction that his real reason for entering the drug-store was not to get a hot chocolate, —not at all! He was going to steal something. He was going to put the impulse to the test, and see whether (*one*) he could manage it with sufficient skill, and (*two*) whether theft gave him any real satisfaction. The drug-store was crowded with people who had just come from the theatre next door. They pushed three deep round the soda fountain, and the cashier's cage. At the back of the store, in the toilet and prescription department, there were not so many, but nevertheless enough to give him a fair chance. All the clerks were busy. His hands were in the side pockets of his overcoat—they were deep wide pockets and would serve admirably. A quick gesture over a table or counter, the object dropped in—

Oddly enough, he was not in the least excited: perhaps that was because of the gin. On the contrary, he was intensely amused; not to say delighted. He was smiling, as he walked slowly along the right-hand side of the store towards the back; edging his way amongst the people, with first one shoulder forward and then the other, while with a critical and appraising eye he examined the wares piled on the counters and on the stands in the middle of the floor. There were some extremely attractive scent-sprays or atomizers—but the dangling bulbs might be troublesome. There were stacks of boxed letter-paper. A basket full of clothes-brushes. Green hot water bottles. Percolators—too large, and out of the question. A tray of multi-colored toothbrushes, bottles of cologne, fountain-pens—and then he experienced love at first sight. There could be no question that he had found his chosen victim. He gazed, fascinated, at the delicious object—a *de luxe* safety-razor set, of heavy gold, in a snakeskin box which was lined with red plush. . . .

It wouldn't do, however, to stare at it too long—one of the clerks might notice. He observed quickly the exact position of the box,—which was close to the edge of the glass counter,—and prefigured with a quite precise mental picture the gesture with which he would simultaneously close it and remove it. Forefinger at the back—thumb in front—the box drawn forward and then slipped down towards the pocket—as he thought it out, the muscles in his forearm pleasurably contracted. He continued his slow progress round the store, past the prescription counter, past the candy counter; examined with some show of attention the display of cigarette lighters and blade sharpeners; and then, with a quick turn, went leisurely back to his victim. Everything was propitious. The whole section of counter was clear for the moment—there were neither customers nor clerks. He approached the counter, leaned over it as if to examine some little filigreed "compacts" at the back of the show-case, picking up one of them with his left hand, as he did so. He was thus leaning directly over the box; and it was the simplest thing in the world to clasp it as planned between the thumb and forefinger of his other hand, to shut it softly, and to slide it downward to his pocket. It was over in an instant. He continued then for a moment to turn the compact case this way and that in the light, as if to see it sparkle. It sparkled very nicely. Then he put it back on the little pile of cases, turned, and approached the soda fountain—just as Hurwitz had suggested.

He was in the act of pressing forward in the crowd to ask for his hot chocolate when he felt a firm hand close round his elbow. He turned, and looked at a man in a slouch hat and dirty raincoat, with the collar turned up. The man was smiling in a very offensive way.

"I guess you thought that was pretty slick," he said in a low voice which nevertheless managed to convey the very essence of venom and hostility. "You come along with me, mister!"

Michael returned the smile amiably, but was a little frightened. His heart began to beat.

"I don't know what you're talking about," he said, still smiling.

"No, of course not!"

The man was walking toward the rear of the store, and was pulling Michael along with him, keeping a paralyzingly tight grip on his elbow. Michael was beginning to be angry, but also to be horrified. He thought of wrenching his arm free, but feared it would make a scene. Better not. He permitted himself to be urged ignominiously along the shop, through a gate in the rear counter, and into a small room at the back, where a clerk was measuring a yellow liquid into a bottle.

"Will you be so kind as to explain to me what this is all about?" he then said, with what frigidity of manner he could muster. But his voice shook a little. The man in the slouch hat paid no attention. He addressed the clerk instead, giving his head a quick backward jerk as he spoke.

"Get the manager in here," he said.

He smiled at Michael, with narrowed eyes, and Michael, hating him, but panic-stricken, smiled foolishly back at him.

"Now, look here—" he said.

But the manager had appeared, and the clerk; and events then happened with revolting and nauseating speed. Michael's hand was yanked violently from his pocket, the fatal snake skin box was pulled out by the detective, and identified by the manager and the clerk. They both looked at Michael with a queer expression, in which astonishment, shame, and contempt were mixed with vague curiosity.

"Sure that's ours," said the manager, looking slowly at Michael.

"I saw him pinch it," said the detective. "What about it?" He again smiled offensively at Michael. "Anything to say?"

"It was all a joke," said Michael, his face feeling very hot and flushed. "I made a kind of bet with some friends. . . . I can prove it. I can call them up for you."

The three men looked at him in silence, all three of them just faintly smiling, as if incredulously.

"Sure you can," said the detective, urbanely. "You can prove it in court. . . . Now come along with me, mister."

Michael was astounded at this appalling turn of events, but his brain still worked. Perhaps if he were to put it to this fellow as man to man, when they got outside? As he was thinking this, he was firmly conducted through a back door into a dark alley at the rear of the store. It had stopped snowing. A cold wind was blowing. But the world, which had looked so beautiful fifteen minutes before, had now lost its charm. They walked together down the alley in six inches of powdery snow, the detective holding Michael's arm with affectionate firmness.

"No use calling the wagon," he said. "We'll walk. It ain't far."

They walked along Tremont Street. And Michael couldn't help, even then, thinking what an extraordinary thing this was! Here were all these good people passing them, and little knowing that he, Michael Lowes, was a thief, a thief by accident, on his way to jail. It seemed so absurd as hardly to be worth speaking of! And suppose they shouldn't believe him? This notion made him shiver. But it wasn't possible—no, it wasn't possible. As soon as he had told his story, and called up Hurwitz and Bryant and Smith, it would all be laughed off. Yes, laughed off.

He began telling the detective about it: how they had discussed such impulses over a game of bridge. Just a friendly game, and they had joked about it and then, just to see what would happen, he had done it. What was it that made his voice sound so insincere, so hollow? The detective neither slackened his pace nor turned his head. His business-like grimness was alarming. Michael felt that he was paying no attention at all; and moreover, it occurred to him that this kind of low-brow official might not even understand such a thing. . . . He decided to try the sentimental.

"And good Lord, man, there's my wife waiting for me—!"

"Oh sure, and the kids too."

"Yes, and the kids!"

The detective gave a quick leer over the collar of his dirty raincoat.

"And no Santy Claus *this* year," he said.

Michael saw that it was hopeless. He was wasting his time.

"I can see it's no use talking to you," he said stiffly. "You're so used to dealing with criminals that you think all mankind is criminal, *ex post facto.*"

"Sure."

Arrived at the station, and presented without decorum to the lieutenant at the desk, Michael tried again. Something in the faces of the lieutenant and the sergeant, as he told his story, made it at once apparent that there was going to be trouble. But after consultation, they agreed to call up Bryant and Hurwitz and Smith, and to make inquiries. The sergeant went off to do this, while Michael sat on a wooden bench. Fifteen minutes passed, during which the clock ticked and the lieutenant wrote slowly in a book, using a blotter very frequently. A clerk had been dispatched also, to look up Michael's record, if any. This gentleman came back first, and reported that there was nothing. The lieutenant scarcely looked up from his book, and went on writing. The first serious blow then fell. The sergeant, reporting, said that he hadn't been able to get Smith (of course—Michael thought—he's off somewhere with Squiggles) but had got Hurwitz and Bryant. Both of them denied that there had been any bet. They both seemed nervous, as far as he could make out over the phone. They said they didn't know Lowes well, were acquaintances of his, and made it clear that they didn't want to be mixed up in anything. Hurwitz had added that he knew Lowes was hard up.

At this, Michael jumped to his feet, feeling as if the blood would burst out of his face.

"The damned liars!" he shouted. "The bloody liars! By God—!"

"Take him away," said the lieutenant, lifting his eyebrows, and making a motion with his pen.

Michael lay awake all night in his cell, after talking for five minutes with Dora on the telephone. Something in Dora's cool voice had frightened him more than anything else.

And when Dora came to talk to him the next morning at nine o'clock, his alarm proved to be well founded. Dora was cold, detached, deliberate. She was not at all what he had hoped she might be—sympathetic and helpful. She didn't volunteer to get a lawyer, or in fact to do anything—and when she listened quietly to his story, it seemed to him that she had the appearance of a person listening to a very improbable lie. Again, as he narrated the perfectly simple episode—the discussion of "impulse" at the bridge-game, the drinks, and the absurd tipsy desire to try a harmless little experiment—again, as when he talked to the store-detective, he heard his own voice becoming hollow and insincere. It was exactly as if he knew himself to be guilty. His throat grew dry, he began to falter, to lose his thread, to use the wrong words. When he stopped speaking, finally, Dora was silent.

"Well, say something!" he said angrily, after a moment. "Don't just stare at me! I'm not a criminal!"

"I'll get a lawyer for you," she answered, "but that's all I can do."

"Look here, Dora—you don't mean you—"

He looked at her incredulously. It wasn't possible that she really thought him a thief? And suddenly, as he looked at her, he realized how long it was since he had really known this woman. They had drifted apart. She was embittered, that was it—embittered by his non-success. All this time she had slowly been laying up a reserve of resentment. She had resented his inability to make money for the children, the little dishonesties they had had to commit in the matter of unpaid bills, the humiliations of duns, the too-frequent removals from town to town— she had more than once said to him, it was true, that because of all this she had never had any friends—and she had resented, he knew, his gay little parties with Hurwitz and Bryant and Smith, implying a little that they were an extravagance which was to say the least inconsiderate. Perhaps they *had* been. But was a man to have no indulgences. . . .?

"Perhaps we had better not go into that," she said.

"Good Lord,—you don't believe me!"

"I'll get the lawyer—though I don't know where the fees are to come from. Our bank account is down to seventy-seven dollars. The rent is due a week from today. You've got some salary coming, of course, but I don't want to touch my own savings, naturally, because the children and I may need them."

To be sure. Perfectly just. Women and children first. Michael thought these things bitterly, but refrained from saying them. He gazed at this queer cold little female with intense curiosity. It was simply extraordinary—simply astonishing. Here she was, seven years his wife, he thought he knew her inside and out, every quirk of her handwriting, inflection of voice; her passion for strawberries, her ridiculous way of singing; the brown moles on her shoulders, the extreme smallness of her feet and toes, her dislike of silk underwear. Her special voice at the telephone, too—that rather chilly abruptness, which had always surprised him, as if she might be a much harder woman than he thought her to be. And the queer sinuous cat-like rhythm with which she always combed her hair before the mirror at night, before going to bed —with her head tossing to one side, and one knee advanced to touch the chest of drawers. He knew all these things, which nobody else knew, and nevertheless, now, they amounted to nothing. The woman herself stood before him as opaque as a wall.

"Of course," he said, "you'd better keep your own savings." His voice was dull. "And you'll of course look up Hurwitz and the others? They'll appear, I'm sure, and it will be the most important evidence. In fact, *the* evidence."

"I'll ring them up, Michael," was all she said, and with that she turned quickly on her heel and went away. . . .

Michael felt doom closing in upon him: his wits went round in circles: he was in a constant sweat. It wasn't possible that he was going to be betrayed? It wasn't possible! He assured himself of this. He walked back and forth, rubbing his hands together, he kept pulling out his watch to see what time it was. Five minutes gone. Another five mintes gone. Damnation, if this lasted too long, this confounded business, he'd lose his job. If it got into the papers, he might lose it anyway. And suppose it was true that

Hurwitz and Bryant had said what they said—maybe they were
afraid of losing their jobs too. Maybe that was it! Good God. . . .
This suspicion was confirmed, when, hours later, the little
Jew lawyer came to see him. He reported that Hurwitz, Bryant,
and Smith had all three refused flatly to be mixed up in the
business. They were all afraid of the effects of the publicity. If
subpoenaed, they said, they would state that they had known
Lowes only a short time, had thought him a little eccentric, and
knew him to be hard up. Obviously—and the little lawyer picked
his teeth with the point of his pencil—they could not be sum-
moned. It would be fatal.

The Judge, not unnaturally perhaps, decided that there was
a perfectly clear case. There couldn't be the shadow of a doubt
that this man had deliberately stolen an article from the counter
of So-and-so's drug-store. The prisoner had stubbornly main-
tained that it was the result of a kind of bet with some friends,
but these friends had refused to give testimony in his behalf.
Even his wife's testimony—that he had never done such a thing
before—had seemed rather half-hearted; and she had admitted,
moreover, that Lowes was unsteady, and that they were always
living in a state of something like poverty. Prisoner, further, had
once or twice jumped his rent and had left behind him in Somer-
ville unpaid debts of considerable size. He was a college man, a
man of exceptional education and origin, and ought to have
known better. His general character might be good enough, but
as against all this, here was a perfectly clear case of theft, and a
perfectly clear motive. The prisoner was sentenced to three
months in the house of correction.

By this time, Michael was in a state of complete stupor. He
sat in the box and stared blankly at Dora who sat very quietly in
the second row, as if she were a stranger. She was looking back
at him, with her white face turned a little to one side, as if she
too had never seen him before, and were wondering what sort of
people criminals might be. Human? Sub-human? She lowered

her eyes, after a moment, and, before she had looked up again, Michael had been touched on the arm and led stumbling out of the courtroom. He thought she would of course come to say good-bye to him, but even in this he was mistaken: she left without a word.

And, when he did finally hear from her, after a week, it was in a very brief note.

"Michael," it said, "I'm sorry but I can't bring up the children with a criminal for a father, so I'm taking proceedings for a divorce. This is the last straw. It was bad enough to have you always out of work and to have to slave night and day to keep bread in the children's mouths. But this is too much, to have disgrace into the bargain. As it is, we'll have to move right away, for the school-children have sent Dolly and Mary home crying three times already. I'm sorry, and you know how fond I was of you at the beginning, but you've had your chance. You won't hear from me again. You've always been a good sport, and generous, and I hope you'll make this occasion no exception, and refrain from contesting the divorce. Good-bye—Dora."

Michael held the letter in his hands, unseeing, and tears came into his eyes. He dropped his face against the sheet of note-paper, and rubbed his forehead to and fro across it . . . Little Dolly! . . . Little Mary! . . . Of course. This was what life was. It was just as meaningless and ridiculous as this; a monstrous joke; a huge injustice. You couldn't trust anybody, not even your wife, not even your best friends. You went on a little lark, and they sent you to prison for it, and your friends lied about you, and your wife left you. . . .

Contest it? Should he contest the divorce? What was the use? There was the plain fact, that he had been convicted for stealing. No one had believed his story of doing it in fun, after a few drinks: the divorce court would be no exception. He dropped the letter to the floor and turned his heel on it, slowly and bitterly. Good riddance—good riddance! Let them all go to hell. He would show them. He would go west, when he came out,—get rich, clear his name somehow. . . . But how?

He sat down on the edge of his bed and thought of Chicago. He thought of his childhood there, the Lake Shore Drive, Winnetka, the trip to Niagara Falls with his mother. He could hear the Falls now. He remembered the Fourth of July on the boat; the crowded examination room at college; the time he had broken his leg in baseball, when he was fourteen, and the stamp collection which he had lost at school. He remembered his mother always saying, "Michael, you *must* learn to be orderly"; and the little boy who had died of scarlet fever next door; and the pink conch-shell smashed in the back yard. His whole life seemed to be composed of such trivial and infinitely charming little episodes as these; and as he thought of them, affectionately and with wonder, he assured himself once more that he had really been a good man. And now, had it all come to an end? It had all come foolishly to an end.

JEROME ELLISON

American Disgrace: College Cheating

Not long ago a professor in a Midwestern university, concerned about evidence of cheating, set up an experiment to discover the extent of it. He gave a difficult assignment and announced there would be a quiz. On the morning of the test he mentioned that the correct answers were on his desk. Then by prearrangement he was called from the room.

Unknown to the others, two graduate students had been enrolled in the class to observe and report on what then might happen. It exceeded the teacher's worst imaginings. No sooner was he out the door than there was a stampede to the desk. With the exception of two dean's-list geniuses, every student present copied the answers and handed them in as his own.

Cheating in college is not, of course, restricted to the Midwest. Students at a large Eastern university recently produced evidence that fraud was so extensive as to raise a doubt whether the institution's examinations and assigned original work had any validity at all. Given the topic "Cheating at This University" as a social-research assignment, they tied into the task with confessional zeal.

There was, it developed, an ingenious assortment of cribbing and signaling devices in everyday use. "Original" written work, sometimes slightly used or from other campuses, was available at four to ten dollars per paper; "tutors" would perform any kind of homework at moderate fees; complete laboratory notes could be obtained without ever having to spend an afternoon in the lab. Examination questions were frequently obtained in advance through theft, pilfering wastebaskets near the duplicating machines, or bribery of staff employees. One student expressed the consensus: "At this school, cheating is standard practice."

The situation would be more reassuring if such places were the exception. Actually, institutions where large-scale, organized cheating has *not* been known are a small minority. The book *Changing Values in College*, the work of a Hazen Foundation committee headed by Philip E. Jacob, of the University of Pennsylvania, who correlated the material in book form, is the most extensive survey of student attitudes undertaken recently. It has this to say: "The chinks in the moral armor of American students are most obvious in regard to cheating. . . . The practice is so widespread as to challenge the well-nigh universal claim of students that they value honesty as a moral virtue. Frequent cheating is admitted by 40 per cent or more [of the students] at a large number of colleges, often with no apology or sense of wrongdoing."

Fairly reliable survey evidence, Professor Jacob wrote to me recently, suggests that one student in three cheats "rather regularly." At the last meeting of the American Council on Education, Dr. Edward D. Eddy Jr., vice president and provost of the University of New Hampshire, told a discussion group that cheating throughout the country "has become a part of the student culture—it's taken for granted."

It has seemed to me, both as a university faculty member and as a citizen, that the matter is of fundamental importance, not only in the educational world but to the country as a whole. Are we becoming a nation of cheaters? If so, whom are we cheating and what are the likely consequences?

Crookedness in politics, in public office, in show business, in commerce, in finance, in sports—all these are old stories to a realistic American public. They are commonly shrugged off as occurring too rarely for real concern, or as the work of an uneducated, pseudocriminal fringe. But large-scale humbug in our seats of higher learning is far more serious. Here we train the nation's moral, intellectual, commercial and professional leaders. Fundamental damage in these vital centers could in today's world climate produce a self-destructive spiral spinning us toward national suicide.

With these feelings at heart this reporter began about a year ago to carry on from where Professor Jacob and his associates left off. Through personal interview, questionnaire, correspondence and survey of the literature, material from coast to coast has accumulated on my desk. It provides a basis for some opinions, not only as to who cheats how often and how, but also as to who has been responsible, and what is demanded to bring it to a halt.

The most common path of academic waywardness is simple copying—plagiarism. Of the many cases in the dossier I select one, from a Midwestern institution, as representative of the attitudes within our educational machinery that make mass cheating possible.

A graduating senior, whom we may call Tom, had been a mediocre student throughout his four years. Required to produce an original paper on some aspect of city management at the close of his final semester, he submitted as his own work a survey of population trends in a certain city. His professor, noting that the paper was better than anything the student had ever done before, became suspicious. A library check revealed that the study had been copied word for word—all but the author's name—from a recent professional journal. The professor ruled plagiarism and failed the student in the course.

Tom appealed the ruling and was given a hearing before a faculty committee. He turned up with a letter from his local clergyman and with two fraternity brothers as character witnesses. The professor involved was not invited. Tom did not deny that he had plagiarized, but asked to be let off on the ground that a failure would prevent him from graduating. The committee ruled in his favor.

It was a major triumph for local cheaters. It served notice to the rank and file of the faculty that even the most flagrant form of academic fraud would not be regarded, on appeal to the governing authorities, as anything very serious. It confirmed student belief that dishonesty would not be penalized even when discovered. As might be expected, cheating is commonplace at this institution.

Two comparable cases occurred at one of the older New England women's colleges. In both instances the guilty students were promptly suspended, as provided by faculty rules, for one semester. These were the only cases of plagiarism reported during a four-year period. The inference—that college and university administrators could put a stop to cheating any time they wanted to—holds throughout the material that has come to my desk.

Why, then, do so many not want to? This question leads, I believe, to the heart of the matter, and must presently be dealt with. But first we ought to explore a little further the various means by which the learning process is diddled.

By far the most common means of cheating is the simple crib, or, in standard usage, illegitimate aid in examinations. Students have written important formulas on sticks of chewing gum, then chewed up the evidence. Scrolls of notes have been rolled into dummy fountain pens, automatic pencils, wrist watches, match covers, cigarette lighters. Data has been written on human skin—palm, or in the case of women students, inside the leg above the knee; and on clothing—dress hems, pants cuffs or sleeves. When tests are given on standard blanks called "blue books," students have smuggled in blanks loaded with basic information; with so many blue books around, the crib is not easily spotted.

Professors who repeat the same tests are easy marks; some cheaters bring their blue books to the examination with their answers already written out. A frequent dodge is the excuse to leave the room during the examination in order to reach a cache of information. A variation of this, worked in a large eastern school which operates on an "honor" system, is for the student to walk back to his room, write correct answers out of the textbook, rush back and turn in the blue book.

These, of course, are all devices of the solitary operator. Gang cheating opens up more extensive possibilities. The principle involved is that someone, either through the possession of a well-informed mind or a good crib, possesses valid information and transmits it—because of fraternal bonds or just to be obliging —to the needy. In one classic case of identical twins, one smart and one dull, the smart one took exams for both!

Often nothing more is required than to hold one's paper so a deficient neighbor can see it. Sometimes, however, intelligence is transmitted to several cheaters through an elaborate signal system. True-and-false and multiple-choice questions can be handled by code. Pen point *up* means true, *down* is false. In multiple-choice, fingers showing at chin level mean number of question; fingers at waist level, number of answer. To prevent leaks some professors are avoiding the duplicating machine, preparing their questions just before the exam and writing them on the board. Cheaters have found the answer to this too. In one system a boy outside reads the multiple-choice questions from the board with field glasses and relays the answers to those near the window by means of hand signals. There must, of course, be a felicitous arrangement of buildings and classrooms for this to succeed.

Even more important than overt cheating, perhaps, is the frame of mind that leads to it. There coexists, side by side with our higher educational system, an actively propagated faith which may be termed "anti-education." Recently in a Boston restaurant I overheard a conversation in which the main tenets of the creed were set forth. A high-school graduate about to set out for college was receiving advice from an upperclassman.

"Now when you get there, remember," the older boy

was saying, "books are for the birds, not for the people. What matters is contacts. Get there a couple, three days early, introduce yourself around, become known, get elected to a class office. Plan your courses so you're not always on the books, so you have time to make contacts."

The younger lad protested that he wanted to be an engineer, a course which called for quite a bit of study along a prescribed curriculum.

"Now, Charley, it's your life, but you ought to get engineering out of your head," the upperclassman said. "It's a grind all four years, morning to night, you're never finished. When you're out of college, does anybody care how many books you read? Make your contacts. Then, man, you got a deal that matters, and if you haven't got that, you got nothing."

The speaker was a fraternity man. He was speaking a philosophy which is heard a great deal around the fraternity houses of the land. Pledges are quite commonly advised to take easy courses and utilize every timesaving short cut. This allows more time for "activities," which are cited during rush week to attract more pledges—time to pursue more activities in an endless antieducational undertow. On many campuses fraternity maintenance of files of past examinations, themes and lab notes is a popular chapter project. Many a fraternity man has planned his four years of "study" around their contents.

Rather a sad case has been made, so far, for the ethical standards of the American college youth. There is abundant evidence, however, that our young people are not happy about it. Not only do they have consciences but these are active and in some cases effective.

It should be noted, for example, that after the "framed" episode described at the opening of this article, students began to call at the professor's office, singly and in pairs, sheepishly admitting that there had been quite a bit of cheating that afternoon and suggesting that nobody would mind taking another quiz on the material. Whereupon the professor confessed that he had deliberately tempted them, and there was mutual forgiveness! Similarly it should be noted that it was the conscience-prompted research of the students that finally laid bare the full extent of cheating in the eastern university mentioned.

Sometimes considerable courage is shown in countering a locally prevailing trend. I know of one fraternity on a campus where cheating is common whose members not only do not cheat but who have withdrawn from all the more frivolous campus activities, making it clear that their purpose in attending college is to learn. National headquarters of almost all fraternities profess concern with scholastic performance. Many local chapters have produced impressive records of honest scholarship. And in some places there is an enduring, campus-wide tradition of strict academic honor. The responsibility of an "honor-system" pledge has been accepted by generations of students at a few institutions.

We return then to the mixed situation already observed. Though cheating is widespread, it isn't universal. Though nobody exactly approves, there is no nationally enforced academic standard to prevent it.

The result, reflected in student questionnaires from East and West, North and South, is a heavy burden of guilt and conflict. "The main trouble is we are afraid to talk for fear of losing standing with the other students; we are against it in principle, but do nothing." (East) . . . "Many don't quite like it morally; it's considered like stealing pennies as a child—not really nice, but hardly a criminal offense." (North Central) . . . "Lots of students would like to see something done about it, but will never openly denounce anyone seen cheating." (East)

The reason for cheating most commonly given is that the pressure to succeed, reinforced by the fear of failure, overwhelms considerations of honor. "The student doesn't realize the seriousness of the act or feel he is hurting anyone by cheating; the grade in the course is his dominant concern." (South Central) . . . "You're under great pressure to make grades for social or family reasons; this leads to desperate means." (South Central) . . . "Here's the situation: I have a *B* in the course, my fraternity brother has a *D;* at exam time I'm supposed to be a good guy and let him sit next to me and copy my paper." (East) . . . "Students are put into a society where the emphasis is on grades rather than on character and integrity—since everyone else cheats he must too, in order to hold his own." (South) . . . "The whole stress is on getting that degree, not on learning." (Midwest) . . . "There is always the pressure of fraternity tradition; upperclassmen do it, freshmen take it as 'the thing to do,' the custom goes on decade after decade." (East)

Many students lay the blame squarely on the faculty: "The faculty pretends to be against cheating, but when it's under their noses they close their eyes and pretend not to see. Though cheating here is continuous, I've only been in one class in three years where a test was picked up for cheating—thirty-five students out of 170 were asked to leave." . . . "Faculty is inconsistent—some members are strict, others act as if they didn't know the meaning of the word 'cheat.'" . . . "There is not enough faculty supervision—too many classes are just mass-production educational assembly lines." . . . "The whole atmosphere of the place is so short on intellectual stimulation that nobody is inspired to do more than go along with the crowd—or leave." . . . "I had a test where the professor was standing four feet away from a student who was copying from sheets clipped from the textbook; he couldn't fail to notice, but did nothing."

Does the faculty have anything to say in its own defense?

An associate professor in one of our Southern universities conceded serious administrative and faculty shortcomings, but did not absolve the students. "As a group, students have resisted every attempt to institute an honor system; almost every period before finals several faculty offices are broken into at night by students attempting to steal examination questions."

The faculty, however, had much to answer for: "We take an attitude of: 'There's no cheating in my department, of course, but it's very prevalent in other departments.' Furthermore, the 'lousy' quality of some of the tests we construct invites cheating. And finally, there's the powerful example of what adults are doing—for example, cheating on income tax."

Administrative officers, our Southern colleague reported, must share the blame. He cited another example of a college administration supporting the cheating student rather than the faculty member attempting to discipline him. "Four instructors independently observed a youngster cheating on a test. We flunked him in the course. He complained to the dean of students, who sent memoranda of rebuke—*to the faculty members!*" They were expected to be "good fellows" and not be too hard on the students.

A prevailing lack of standards in all fields was cited as the prime cause of collegiate fraud: "Americans seem to have few or no values, especially those of self-control, by which to live. For example, there were recent news stories of price-fixing by large corporations, as they submitted identical bids on a public-works project. This seems to be perfectly acceptable behavior unless there is a specific law against it. Our shenanigans and double talk are observed by young people."

Another professor, who has had experience at two Mid-western state universities and now teaches at an Eastern school, finds at least part of the trouble within the faculty and administration. "Many studies have been done showing how widespread cheating is. There have been cases where school officials hush them up for reasons having to do with politics and the good university name." Professors as a class, he thinks, are not really exercised about the matter: "They often say, 'Let them cheat. The ones who came for an education will get it anyway.'"

A department head at a small Southern junior college dissents: "The faculty here is genuinely concerned; several meetings have been given over to discussions of the cheating problem." He finds student anxiety stemming mainly from lacks in the precollege educational background—and the cheating stemming from the anxiety. A dean at one of Ohio's many large coeducational colleges, reporting on a faculty-student conference, rated the causes in about this order: "Lazy students, lazy professors, importance of grades over knowledge, pressure to get into professional schools."

The dean of students at a big Southern university confesses faculty uncertainty: "They are skeptical about methods of apprehending offenders." As for the main cause of cheating, he tosses responsibility back on the student: "Poor background, lack of a sense of honor and personal integrity, lack of ability to do college work."

Professor Jacob of Pennsylvania, whose book has been previously mentioned, splits the blame between faculty and student. He finds the prime causes of cheating to be "over-emphasis on grade-exam procedures and a widespread student tradition of tolerance toward the practice."

Now we are ready for the inevitable question. What have I to say on my own account? As a member of a university faculty, it would be strange if I had not formed some opinions.

Professor Jacob's book contains an interesting chapter titled, "The Peculiar Potency of Some Colleges." In it he notes the extraordinary effectiveness of some institutions in producing superior graduates, and the high academic morale that prevails on their campuses. Students in one place "have a high regard for their college education and do not cheat." In another, "the touch of the institution's special influence has been felt." Students of a third would "like to make a contribution to society for which they would be remembered." At a fourth, "love of people and altruism became the pre-eminent values for seniors." What can be done, Professor Jacob wants to know, to inspire more of our colleges and universities to such high attainment?

In reply I would suggest that a university, like a person, ought to stand for something. Each of the "peculiarly potent" schools stood for a high intellectual and moral precept. At such institutions short shrift is given to cheaters, and faculty members are not reprimanded or reversed on appeal, when they deal firmly with them.

The first step in a school concerned about its cheating, I would think, should be to ask itself what it stands for. Does it rest its reputation on having the biggest enrollment in its state? As fielding the best football team? As offering the greatest

variety of courses? As having the handsomest fraternity houses
and the most luxurious student-union building? None of these
things, I suggest, offers the kind of challenge required. The
school must assign itself some inspired goal, some lofty set of aims
which has won the passionate loyalty of a dedicated faculty.
These aims, whatever may be their specific nature, should have
their roots in an undeviating allegiance to the truth.

The practical, national impotence of truth is, I think, too
little recognized. I am speaking now, not of ideals that tend to
become fuzzily poetic, but of the hard-headed business of getting
along in the job of being a nation. Because so many trades yield
success with few demands on precision, we have come to think
that shading things a little to one side of the truth doesn't greatly
matter.

This is to lose sight of the fact that we must depend more and
more in our nationally crucial ventures upon accurate knowledge. For example, the lessons of history, correctly interpreted,
are vital to the national safety. But if our historians are sloppy
workmen, who will tell us of such things? The space age demands rockets that will work, and these are not produced by
designers who won their A's in math by cheating. The surgeon
at the operating table needs knowledge, not just a grade. There
is an ever-increasing number of fields where fooling with the
truth, either through incompetence or fraud, can produce disaster. If the repositories of knowledge have grown careless about
the truth, we are undone. It is somewhat as if a nation backing
its currency with gold discovered that its vaults contained only
pig iron.

The same regard for truth that produces intellectual great-
ness can also reduce the anxiety that apparently drives so many
students to cut corners. The new national demand of a college
diploma for every child is bound to bring some disappointments.
Not everyone—as shown by a national dropout rate of 60 per
cent in four years—is capable of winning a university degree.
Accepting one's limitations is surely one form of accepting truth.

Surely those honest ones who failed in college have a right

to leave there without feeling that they have failed in life. Some of the most exalted chapters of human history, they should understand, have been contributed, and are still being contributed, without benefit of diploma. There is vital work to be done that does not require a college degree.

But those who have chosen to strive for this honor, and those who bestow it, need to understand the gravity of what they are doing. Knowledge is the true currency of our time. The college diploma is one token of knowledge. If, through cheating, it is turned counterfeit at the mint, we are bankrupt.

MARGARET WEYMOUTH JACKSON

The Hero

Mr. Whalen came into the kitchen by the back door and closed it softly behind him. He looked anxiously at his wife.

"Is Marv in?" he asked.

"He's resting," she whispered. Mr. Whalen nodded. He tiptoed through the dining room and went into the front hall as quiet as a mouse, and hung his hat and coat away. But he could not resist peeking into the darkened living room. A fire burned on the hearth, and on the couch lay a boy, or young man, who looked, at first glance, as though he were at least seven feet tall. He had a throw pulled up around his neck, and his stocking feet stuck out from the cuffs of his corduroy trousers over the end of the sofa.

"Dad?" a husky young voice said.

"Yes. Did I waken you? I'm sorry."

"I wasn't sleeping. I'm just resting."

Mr. Whalen went over to the couch and looked down at the long figure with deep concern.

"How do you feel?" he asked tenderly.

"Swell, Dad. I feel fine. I feel as though I'm going to be lucky tonight."

"That's fine! That's wonderful!" said his father fervently.

"What time is it, Dad?"

"Quarter to six."

"About time for me to get up and have my supper. Is it ready? I ought to stretch a bit."

"You lie still now, Marv. I'll see about your supper."

Mr. Whalen hurried back into the kitchen. "He's awake," he informed his wife. "Is his supper ready?"

"In a minute, dear. I'm just making his tea."

Mr. Whalen went back into the living room with his anxious, bustling air.

The young man was up from the couch. He had turned on the light in a table lamp. He was putting on his shoes. He looked very young, not more than sixteen. His hair was thick as taffy and about the same color. He was thin, with a nose a little too big, and with clear blue eyes and a pleasant mouth and chin. He was not especially handsome, except to his father, who thought him the finest-looking boy in the whole wide world. The boy looked up a little shyly and smiled, and somehow his father's opinion was justified.

"I couldn't hit a thing in short practice yesterday," Marvin said. "That means I'll be hot tonight. Red-hot!"

"I hope so. I certainly hope so."

"You're going to the game, aren't you, Dad? You and Mother?"

Wild horses couldn't have kept Mr. Whalen away.

Marvin rose from his chair. He went up and up and up. Six feet four in his stocking feet, a hundred and seventy-six pounds, and sixteen years of age. Marvin flexed his muscles, crouched a little, and made a twisting leap into the air, one arm going up over his head in a swinging circle, his hand brushing the ceiling. He landed lightly as a cat. His father watched him, appearing neither astonished nor amused. There was nothing but the most profound respect and admiration in Mr. Whalen's eyes.

"We've been timing that pivot. Mr. Leach had two guards on me yesterday and they couldn't hold me, but I couldn't hit. Well, Dad, let's eat. I ought to be getting up to the gym."

They went into the kitchen, where the supper was laid on a

clean cloth at a small round table. There was steak and potatoes and salad and chocolate cake for his parents, toast and tea and coddled eggs for the boy.

"I don't think you ought to put the cake out where Marv can see it, when he can't have any," fussed Mr. Whalen.

Marvin grinned. "It's okay, Dad. I don't mind. I'll eat some when I get home."

"Did you take your shower? Dry yourself good?"

"Sure, Dad. Of course."

"Was the doctor at school today? This was the day he was to check the team, wasn't it?"

"Yes. He was there, I'm okay. The arch supports Mr. Leach sent for came. You know, my left foot's been getting a little flat. Doc thought I ought to have something while I'm still growing."

"It's a good thing. Have you got them here?"

"Yes. I'll get them."

"No. Just tell me where they are. I'll look at them."

"In my room. In my gym shoes."

Mr. Whalen wasn't eating a bite of supper. It just gave him indigestion to eat on game nights. He got too excited. He couldn't stand it. The boy was eating calmly. He ate four coddled eggs. He ate six pieces of toast. He drank four cups of tea with lemon and sugar. In the boy's room Mr. Whalen checked the things in his bag—the white woolen socks, the clean folded towel, the shoes with their arch supports, and so on. The insets looked all right, his father thought. The fine, heavy satin playing suits would be packed in the box in which they came from the dry cleaner's, to keep them from getting wrinkled before the game.

There, alone in Marvin's room, with Marvin's ties hanging on his dresser, with his windbreaker thrown down in a chair and his high school books on the table, Mr. Whalen felt a little ill. He pressed his hand over his heart. He mustn't show his anxiety, he thought. The boy was calm. He felt lucky. Mustn't break that feeling. Mr. Whalen went back into the kitchen with an air of cheer, a plump, middle-aged man with a retreating hairline and kind, anxious, brown eyes. Mr. Whalen was a few inches shorter than his wife. But he had never regretted marrying a tall woman. Look at his boy!

Marv was looking at the funnies in the evening paper. Mr. Whalen resisted the temptation to look at the kitchen clock. The boy would know when to go. He took the front part of the paper and sat down and tried to put his mind on the news. Mrs. Whalen quietly washed the supper dishes. Marvin finished the funnies in the local paper and handed it to his father. Mr. Whalen took it and read the news that Hilltown High was to play Sunset High, of Stone City, at the local gym that evening. The Stone City team hadn't lost a game. They were grooming for the state championship. Mr. Whalen felt weak. He hoped Marvin hadn't read this. Indignation grew in the father, as he read on down the column, that the odds were against the local team. How dare Mr. Minton print such nonsense for the boys to read—to discourage them? It was outrageous. Mr. Whalen would certainly give the editor a piece of his mind. Perhaps Marvin had read it and believed it! Everything was so important—the psychology wasn't good.

Marvin had finished the funnies in the city paper, and he put it down and rose. He said a little ruefully, "I'm still hungry, but I can't eat more now."

"I'll have something ready for you when you get home," his mother said.

Marvin went into his room and came back in his windbreaker, his hair combed smoothly on his head.

"I'll see you at the gym," he said. "Sit where you always do, will you, Dad?"

"Yes. Yes. We'll be there."

"Okay. I'll be seeing you."

"Don't you want me to take you down in the car?"

"No. Thanks, Dad, but no. It'll do me good to run down there. It won't take me but a minute."

A shrill whistle sounded from the street.

"There's Johnny." Marvin left at once.

Mr. Whalen looked at his watch. "Better hurry, Mother. The first game starts at seven. We won't get our regular seats if we're late."

"I'm not going to the gym at half-past six," said Mrs. Whalen definitely. "We'll be there in time, and no one will take our seats. If you don't calm down, you are going to have a stroke at one of these games."

"I'm perfectly calm," said Mr. Whalen indignantly; "I'm as calm as—as calm as a June day. That's how calm I am. You know I'm not of a nervous temperament. Just because I want to get to the game on time, you say I am excited. You're as up in the air as I am."

"I am not," said Mrs. Whalen. She sat down at the cleared table and looked at the advertisements in the paper. Mr. Whalen looked at his watch again. He fidgeted.

"You can go ahead, if you like," she said. "I'll come alone."

"No, no," he protested, "I'll wait for you. Do you think we had better take the car? I put it up, but I can get it out again."

"We'll walk," she said. "It will do you good—quiet your nerves."

"I'm not nervous," he almost shouted. Then he subsided again, muttered a little, pretended to read the paper, checked his watch against the kitchen clock to see if it had stopped.

"If we're going to walk . . ." he said in a minute.

Mrs. Whalen looked at him with pity. He couldn't help it, she knew. She folded the papers and put them away, took off her white apron, smoothed her hair, and went to get her wraps. Mr. Whalen was at the front door, his overcoat on, his hat in his hand. She deliberately pottered, getting the cat off the piano and putting him out of doors, locking the kitchen door, turning out lights, hunting for her gloves. Mr. Whalen was almost frantic by the time she joined him on the front porch. They went down the walk together, and when they reached the sidewalk they met neighbors also bound for the gym.

"How's Marv?" asked the man next door. "Is he all right?"

"Marv's fine, just fine. He couldn't be better."

"Boy, oh, boy," said the other enthusiastically, "would I like to see the boys whip Stone City! It would be worth a million dollars—a cool million. Stone City thinks no one can beat them. We'd burn the town down."

"Oh, this game doesn't matter so much," said Mr. Whalen deprecatingly. "The team is working toward the tournaments. Be a shame to show all their stuff tonight."

"Well, we'll see. We'll see."

They went ahead. At the next corner they met other friends. "How's Marv? How's the big boy?"

"He's fine. He's all right." Mr. Whalen's chest expansion increased. Cars were parked all along the sidewalk before the group of township school buildings—the grade school and the high school, with the fine brick gymnasium between them. The walks were crowded now, for the whole town, except those in wheel chairs or just born, went to the games, and this was an important game with Hilltown's hereditary foe. Mr. Whalen grew very anxious about their seats. If Marvin looked around for them and didn't find them . . . He hurried his wife a little. They went into the outer hall of the gymnasium. The school principal was standing there talking to the coach, Mr. Leach. Mr. Whalen's heart plummeted. Had anything gone wrong? Had something happened to Marvin? He looked at them anxiously, but they spoke in normal tones.

"Good evening, Mrs. Whalen. Good evening, Tom."

Several small boys were running up and down the stairs, and the school principal turned and spoke to them severely. The Whalens had to make room for a young married couple, he carrying a small baby, she holding the hand of a little boy. Then they reached the window where the typing teacher was tearing off ticket stubs. Mr. Whalen paid his half dollar and they went inside the iron bar and up the steps to the gym proper.

The gymnasium wasn't half full. The bleachers which rose on either side of the shining, sacred floor with its cabalistic markings were spotted with people. The Hilltown eighth grade was playing the Sugar Ridge eighth grade. The boys scrambled, fell

down, got up, and threw the ball, panted and heaved and
struggled on the floor. A basketball flew about. A group of
smaller children were seated in a tight knot, and two little girls
whose only ambition in life was to become high school cheerleaders led a piercing yell:

> *Hit 'em high,*
> *Hit 'em low;*
> *Come on, eighth grade,*
> *Let's go!*

The voices of the junior high were almost piping. Mr.
Whalen remembered how he had suffered when Marvin was in
the eighth grade and they had to go to the games at six o'clock
to watch him play. The junior-high games were very abbreviated,
with six-minute quarters, which was all the state athletic association would let them play. Marvin had been five feet ten at
thirteen, but too thin. He had put on a little weight in proportion
to his height since then, but his father thought he should be
heavier. The present eighth-grade team could not compare with
Marvin's, Mr. Whalen decided.

But the boys did try hard. They were winning. The gun
sounded, the junior high went to pieces with wild cheering, and
the teams trotted off the floor, panting, sweating, happy.

Almost at once another group came on in secondhand white
wool tops and the old blue satin trunks from last year. This was
the second team. The boys were pretty good. They practiced,
throwing the ball from far out, running in under the basket,
passing to one another. Mr. and Mrs. Whalen had found their
regular seats unoccupied, halfway between the third and fourth
uprights which supported the lofty gymnasium ceiling. Mr.
Whalen sat down a little weakly and wiped his forehead. Mrs.
Whalen began at once to visit with a friend sitting behind her,
but Mr. Whalen could not hear what anyone said.

The Stone City reserves came out on the floor to warm up.
They looked like first-string men.

Mr. Leach was talking to the timekeeper. He was a good coach—a mighty good coach. They were lucky to keep him here at Hilltown. The luckiest thing that had ever happened to the town was when Mr. Leach had married a Hilltown girl who didn't want to move away. They'd never have been able to hold him otherwise. It meant so much to the boys to have a decent, kindly man to coach them. Some of the high school coaches felt that their teams had to win, no matter how. It would be very bad to have his boy under such an influence, thought Mr. Whalen, who simply could not bear to see the team defeated, and who was always first to yell "Thief!" and "Robber!"

The officials came out in their green shirts, and Mr. Whalen almost had heart failure. There was that tall, thin man who had fouled Marvin every time he had moved in the tournaments last year. He was always against Hilltown. He had been so unfair that Mr. Leach had complained about him to the state association. The only time Mr. Leach had ever done such a thing. Oh, this was awful. Mr. Whalen twisted his hat in his hands. The other official he had seen often. He was fair—very fair. Sugar Ridge had complained about him for favoring Hilltown, but Mr. Whalen thought him an excellent referee.

The gymnasium was filling fast now. All the high school students—two hundred of them—were packed in the cheering section. The junior high was swallowed up, lost. The cheering section looked as though not one more could get into it, and yet youngsters kept climbing up, squeezing in. The rest of the space was filled with townspeople, from toddlers in snow suits to gray-bearded dodderers. On the opposite side of the gymnasium, the visiting fans were filling their seats. Big crowd from Stone City. Businessmen and quarrymen and stone carvers and their wives and children. They must feel confident of winning, Mr. Whalen thought. Their cheerleaders were out on the floor. Where were Hilltown's? Ah, there they were—Beth and Mary. Hilltown's cheerleaders were extremely pretty adolescents dressed in blue satin slacks with white satin shirts, the word "Yell" in blue letters over their shoulders—a true gilding of the lily. Mary was Marvin's girl. She was the prettiest girl in town. And she had personality, too, and vigor.

Now the two girls leaped into position, spun their hands, spread out their arms, catapulted their bodies into the air in perfect synchronization, and the breathless cheering section came out in a long roll.

> *Hello, Stone City,*
> *Hello, Stone City,*
> *Hilltown says,*
> *Hello-o-o-!*

Not to be outdone, the Stone City leaders, in crimson-and-gold uniforms, returned the compliment:

> *Hello, Hilltown . . .*

and the sound came nicely across the big gym. Mr. Whalen got a hard knot in his throat, and the bright lights and colors of the gymnasium swam in a mist. He couldn't help it. They were so young. Their voices were so young!

The whistle blew. The reserves were at it.

Mr. Whalen closed his eyes and sat still. It would be so long; the cheering wouldn't really start, the evening wouldn't begin until the team came out. He remembered when Marvin was born. He had been tall then—twenty-two inches. Mr. Whalen prayed, his lips moving a little, that Marvin wouldn't get hurt tonight. Suppose he had a heart attack and fell dead, like that boy at Capital City years ago. Suppose he got knocked against one of the steel uprights and hurt his head—damaged his brain? Suppose he got his knee injured? Mr. Whalen opened his eyes. He must not think of those things. He had promised his wife he would not worry so. He felt her hand, light but firm, on his arm.

"Here are the Lanes," she said.

Mr. Whalen spoke to them. Johnny's parents crowded in behind the Whalens. Johnny's father's hand fell on Mr. Whalen's shoulder.

"How's Marv tonight?"

"Fine, fine. How's Johnny?"

"Couldn't be better. I believe the boys are going to take them.

The two fathers looked at each other and away. Mr. Whalen felt a little better.

"How's business?" asked Johnny's father, and they talked about business a moment or two, but they were not interested.

There was a crisis of some kind on the floor. Several players were down in a pile. Someone was hurt. Mr. Whalen bit the edge of his felt hat. The boy was up now. The Stone City coach was out on the floor, but the boy shook his head. He was all right. The game was resumed.

At last it was over. The reserves had won. Mr. Whalen thought that was a bad omen. The eighth grade had won. The reserves had won. No, it was too much. The big team would lose. If the others had lost, he would have considered that a bad omen too. Every omen was bad to Mr. Whalen at this stage. The floor was empty. The high school band played "Indiana," and "Onward, Hilltown," and everyone stood up and sang.

There was a breathless pause, and then a crashing cheer hit the ceiling of the big gym and bounced back. The Team was out. Out there on the floor in their blue satin suits, with jackets over their white tops, warming up, throwing the ball deftly about. What caused the change? Mr. Whalen never knew, but everything was quick now, almost professional in tone and quality. Self-confidence, authority, had come into the gymnasium. Ten or twelve boys out there warming up. But there was really only one boy on the floor for Mr. Whalen, a tall, thin, fair boy with limber legs still faintly brown from summer swimming. Mr. Whalen did not even attempt to tear his eyes from Marvin.

The Stone City team came out. Mr. Whalen looked away from Marvin for a moment to study them. Two or three of them were as tall as Marvin, maybe taller. He felt indignant. They must be seniors, all of them. Or five-year men. He studied

the boys. He liked to see if he could pick out the first-string men
from the lot. He could almost always do it—not by their skill or
their height, but by their faces. That little fellow with the pug
nose—he was a first-string man. And the two big ones—the other
tall man Mr. Whalen discarded correctly. And the boy with the
thick chest. What it was, he wasn't sure—some carelessness, some
ease that marked the first-string men. The others were always a
little self-conscious, a little too eager.

The referee blew the whistle. The substitutes left the floor,
carrying extra jackets. The boy with the pug nose came forward
for Stone City. So he was captain? Mr. Whalen felt gratified in
his judgment. Marvin came forward for his team. He was captain
too. There was a Number 1 in blue on the sleeveless white satin
shirt he wore. The referee talked to them. The boys took their
positions, the umpire his along the edge of the floor. The cheering section roared:

> *We may be rough,*
> *We may be tough,*
> *But we're the team*
> *That's got the stuff!*
> *Fight! Fight! Fight!*

Mary turned a complete somersault, her lithe young body
going over backward, her heels in the air, then hitting the floor
to bounce her straight up in a spread eagle. Her pretty mouth was
open in a square. The rooting swelled. The substitutes sat down
with their coaches. Marvin stood back out of the center ring
until the referee, ball in hand, waved him in. The ball went into
the air as the whistle blew, and the game was on.

Marvin got the tip-off straight to Johnny. Marv ran down
into the corner, where he circled to confuse his guard. Johnny
brought the ball down over the line, faked a pass and drew
out Marvin's guard, bounced the ball to Perk, who carried it
almost to the foul line and passed to Marvin, who threw the ball
into the basket. Stone City leaped outside, threw the ball in, a
long pass. Perk leaped for it, but missed. The tall Stone City

forward dribbled, dodging skillfully. The guards were smothering him, but he pivoted, flung the ball over his head and into the basket. A basket each in the first minute of play!

Mr. Whalen had stopped breathing. He was in a state of suspended animation. The game was very fast—too fast. Stone City scored a second and a third time. Marvin called time out. Someone threw a wet towel from the bench, and it slid along the floor. The boys wiped their faces with it, threw it back. They whispered together. The referee blew the whistle. Yes, they were going to try the new trick play they had been practicing. It worked. Marvin's pivot was wonderful. The score was four to six.

Marvin played with a happy romping abandon. He was skillful, deft, acute. But he was also gay. The youngsters screamed his name. Mr. Whalen saw Mary's rapt, adoring look. Marvin romped down the floor like a young colt.

At the end of the quarter, the score was fourteen to ten in Stone City's favor. At the end of the half, it was still in Stone City's favor, but only fourteen to thirteen. Stone City didn't score in the second quarter.

Mr. Whalen felt a deep disquietude. He had been watching the tall center on the other team, the pivot man. He had thick, black, curly hair and black eyes. Mr. Whalen thought he looked tough. He had fouled Marvin twice in the first half. That is, he had been called for two fouls, but he had fouled him oftener. Mr. Whalen was sure he had tripped Marvin that time Marvin fell on the floor and cracked his elbow. Marvin had jumped up again at once. The Stone City center was a dirty player and ought to be taken off the floor. The school band was playing, but Mr. Whalen couldn't hear it. He was very upset. If the referees were going to let Stone City foul Hilltown and get away with it . . . He felt hot under the collar. He felt desperate.

"Why don't you go out and smoke?" his wife asked. Mr. Whalen folded his overcoat to mark his place and went out of the gym. He smoked two cigarettes as fast as he could. He would stay out here. The stars were cool and calm above his head. The night air was fresh. He couldn't stand it in the gymnasium. He would wait here until the game was over. If Marvin was hurt, he wouldn't see it. He resolved this firmly. But when the whistle blew and he heard the burst of cheering, he rushed back into the gymnasium like a man going to a fire.

The second half had begun. Again the big center fouled Marvin. Marvin got two free throws and made both good.

Fifteen to fourteen now! The crowd went wild. The game got very fast again. Mr. Whalen watched Marvin and his opponent like a hawk. There! It happened.

Mr. Whalen was on his feet, yelling, "Watch him! Watch him!"

The Stone City center had driven his elbow into Marvin's stomach. Marvin was doubled up. Marvin was down on the floor. A groan went up from the bleachers. Mr. Whalen started out on the floor. Something held him. He looked around blindly. His wife had a firm grip on his coat-tails. She gave him a smart yank and pulled him unexpectedly down on the bench beside her.

"He doesn't want you on the floor," she said fiercely.

Mr. Whalen was very angry, but he controlled himself. He sat still. Marvin was up again. Mary led a cheer for him. Marvin was all right. He got two more free throws. Now Hilltown was three points ahead. Marvin was fouled again, got two more free throws and missed them both. He was hurt! He never missed free throws—well, hardly ever. What was the matter with the referee? Was he crazy? Was he bribed? Mr. Whalen groaned.

Stone City took time out, and in the last minute of the third quarter they made three quick baskets. It put them ahead again, three points. A foul was called on Marvin—for pushing.

"Why, he never did at all!" yelled Mr. Whalen. "He couldn't stop fast enough—that's not a foul! Just give them the ball, boys! Don't try to touch it!"

"Will you hush?" demanded his wife.

The Stone City forward made one of the two throws allowed. It was the quarter.

The game was tied three times in the last quarter. With five minutes to play, the big center fouled Marvin again. His last personal. He was out of the game. The Hilltown crowd booed him. None so loud as Mr. Whalen, who often talked long and seriously to Marvin about sportsmanship.

Then Marvin got hot. He couldn't miss. Everyone on the team fed him the ball, and he could throw it from anywhere and it went, plop, right into the basket. Marvin pivoted. His height, his spring, carried him away from his guards. Marvin pranced. His long legs carried him where he would. He threw the ball over his head and from impossible angles. Once he was knocked down on the floor, and he threw from there and made the basket. His joy, his perfection, his luck, caused the crowd to burst into continuous wild cheering. Stone City took time out. They ran in substitutes, but they couldn't stop Marvin. Perk would recover the ball; he and Johnny fed it skillfully to Marvin, and Marvin laid it in. The gun went off with Hilltown twelve points ahead.

Mr. Whalen was a wreck. He could hardly stand up. Mrs. Whalen took his arm and half supported him toward the stairs that led down to the school grounds. The Stone City fans were angry. A big, broad-shouldered man with fierce black eyes complained in a loud, quarrelsome voice:

"That skinny kid—that Whalen boy—he fouled my boy! Who cares? But when my boy protects himself, what happens? They put him off the floor. They put my Guido out, so Hilltown wins. I get my hands on that tall monkey and I'll fix him."

"Be careful. That's my son you're talking about." The strength had returned to Mr. Whalen. He was strong as a lion. Mrs. Whalen pulled at his arm, but he jerked away. He turned on the crowded stairs. "Before you do anything to Marvin," he said, his voice loud and high, "you'd better do something to me. Your son fouled repeatedly."

"That's a lie!" yelled the other, and Mr. Whalen hit him. He hit him right in the stomach as hard as he could punch him. Instantly there was a melee. Johnny's father was punching somebody, and for a moment the crowd heaved and milled on the stairs. Someone screamed. Something like a bolt of lightning hit Mr. Whalen in the eye, and he struck back.

Friends were pulling him away. The town marshal shouldered good-naturedly between the combatants. The big man was in the grip of others from Stone City, who dragged him back up the stairs. Mr. Whalen struggled with his captors, fellow townsmen, who sympathized with him but had no intention of letting him fight. Johnny's mother and Marvin's mother hustled their men out into the cold night air.

"Really!" the high school principal was saying anxiously. "Really, we mustn't have any trouble. The boys don't fight. If we could just keep the fathers away from the games! Really, Mrs. Whalen, this won't do."

"I've got a good notion to take a poke at him too," said Mr. Whalen, who was clear above himself.

In the kitchen, Mr. Whalen looked in a small mirror at his reflection. He felt wonderful. He felt marvelous. He was going to have a black eye. He grabbed his wife and kissed her soundly.

"They beat them!" he said. "They beat Stone City!"

"You old fool!" cried Mrs. Whalen. "I declare I'd be ashamed of Marvin if he acted like that. You and Johnny's father—fighting like hoodlums."

"I don't care!" said Mr. Whalen. "I'm glad I hit him. Teach him a lesson. I feel great. I'm hungry. Make some coffee, Mother."

Marvin wouldn't be in for an hour. He would have a date with Mary at the soda parlor, to which the whole high school would repair. They heard the siren blowing, they looked out of the window and saw the reflection of the bonfire on the courthouse lawn. They heard the fire engine. The team was having a ride on the fire engine. Mr. Whalen stood on his front porch and cheered. The town was wild with joy. Not a citizen that wasn't up in the air tonight.

At last Marvin came in. He was cheerful, practical. "Did you really have a fight, Dad? Someone told me you popped Guido's father. . . . Boy, are you going to have a shiner!" Marvin was greatly amused. He examined his father's eye, recommended an ice pack.

"I want it to get black," said Mr. Whalen stubbornly.

"We sure fixed Guido," said Marvin, and laughed.

"Did you have a fight?" asked his father eagerly.

"Heck, no! I'm going to get him a date with Betty. He noticed her. He's coming up next Sunday. Their team went downtown for sodas because Guido wanted to meet Betty. I wasn't sore at him. I only mean he was easy to handle. I saw right away that I could make him foul me, give me extra shots, get him off the floor. It's very easy to do with a big clumsy guy like that."

Mr. Whalen fingered his swelling eye and watched Marvin eat two hot ham sandwiches and a big slab of chocolate cake and drink a quart of milk. Marvin had already had a soda.

"You must sleep late in the morning," Mr. Whalen said. "Maybe you got too tired tonight. Now, don't eat too much cake."

Mr. Whalen's eye hurt. Mrs. Whalen got him to bed and put a cold compress on it.

"Old ninny," she murmured, and stooped and kissed him. Mr. Whalen sighed. He was exhausted. He was getting too old to play basketball, he thought confusedly.

SHIRLEY JACKSON

Strangers in Town

I don't gossip. If there is anything in this world I loathe, it is gossip. A week or so ago in the store, Dora Powers started to tell me that nasty rumor about the Harris boy again, and I came right out and said to her if she repeated one more word of that story to me I wouldn't speak to her for the rest of my life, and I haven't. It's been a week and not one word have I said to Dora Powers, and that's what I think of gossip. Tom Harris has always been too easy on that boy anyway; the young fellow needs a good whipping and he'd stop all this ranting around, and I've said so to Tom Harris a hundred times and more.

If I didn't get so mad when I think about that house next door, I'd almost have to laugh, seeing people in town standing in the store and on corners and dropping their voices to talk about fairies and leprechauns, when every living one of them knows there isn't any such thing and never has been, and them just racking their brains to find new tales to tell. I don't hold with gossip, as I say, even if it's about leprechauns and fairies, and it's my held opinion that Jane Dollar is getting feeble in the mind. The Dollars weren't ever noted for keeping their senses right up to the end anyway, and Jane's no older than her mother was when she sent a cake to the bake sale and forgot to put the eggs in it. Some said she did it on purpose to get even with the ladies for not asking her to take a booth, but most just said the old lady had lost track of things, and I dare say she could have looked out and seen fairies in her garden if it ever came into her mind. When the Dollars get that age, they'll tell anything, and that's right where Jane Dollar is now, give or take six months.

My name is Addie Spinner, and I live down on Main Street, the last house but one. There's just one house after mine, and then Main Street kind of runs off into the woods—Spinner's Thicket, they call the woods, on account of my grandfather building the first house in the village. Before the crazy people moved in, the house past mine belonged to the Bartons, but they moved away because he got a job in the city, and high time, too, after them living off her sister and her husband for upward of a year.

Well, after the Bartons finally moved out—owing everyone in town, if you want my guess—it wasn't long before the crazy people moved in, and I knew they were crazy right off when I saw that furniture. I already knew they were young folks, and probably not married long because I saw them when they came to look at the house. Then when I saw the furniture go in I knew there was going to be trouble between me and her.

The moving van got to the house about eight in the morning. Of course, I always have my dishes done and my house swept up long before that, so I took my mending for the poor out on the side porch and really got caught up on a lot I'd been letting slide. It was a hot day, so I just fixed myself a salad for my lunch, and the side porch is a nice cool place to sit and eat on a hot day, so I never missed a thing going into that house.

First, there were the chairs, all modern, with no proper legs and seats, and I always say that a woman who buys herself that flyaway kind of furniture has no proper feeling for her house— for one thing, it's too easy to clean around those little thin legs; you can't get a floor well-swept without a lot of hard work. Then, she had a lot of low tables, and you can't fool me with

them—when you see those little low tables, you can always tell
there's going to be a lot of drinking liquor go on in that house;
those little tables are made for people who give cocktail parties
and need a lot of places to put glasses down. Hattie Martin, she
has one of those low tables, and the way Martin drinks is a crime.
Then when I saw the barrels going in next door, I was sure. No
one just married has that many dishes without a lot of cocktail
glasses, and you can't tell me any different.

When I went down to the store later, after they were all
moved in, I met Jane Dollar, and I told her about the drinking
that was going to go on next door, and she said she wasn't a bit
surprised because the people had a maid. Not someone to come
one day a week and do the heavy cleaning—a maid. Lived in the
house and everything. I said I hadn't noticed any maid, and Jane
said most things if I hadn't noticed them she wouldn't believe
they existed in this world, but the Wests' maid was sure enough;
she'd been in the store not ten minutes earlier buying a chicken.
We didn't think she'd rightly have time enough to cook a
chicken before suppertime, but then we decided that probably
the chicken was for tomorrow, and tonight the Wests were
planning on going over to the inn for dinner and the maid could
fix herself an egg or something. Jane did say that one trouble
with having a maid—Jane never had a maid in her life, and I
wouldn't speak to her if she did—was that you never had anything left over. No matter what you planned, you had to get new
meat every day.

I looked around for the maid on my way home. The quickest
way to get to my house from the store is to take the path that
cuts across the back garden of the house next door, and even
though I don't use it generally—you don't meet neighbors to pass
the time of day with, going along a back path—I thought I'd
better be hurrying a little to fix my own supper, so I cut across
the Wests' back garden. West, that was their name, and what the
maid was called I didn't know, because Jane hadn't been able to
find out. It was a good thing I did take the path, because there

was the maid, right out there in the garden, down on her hands and knees, digging.

"Good evening," I said, just as polite as I could. "It's kind of damp to be down on the ground."

"I don't mind," she said. "I like things that grow."

I must say she was a pleasant-speaking woman, although too old, I'd think, for domestic work. The poor thing must have been in sad straits to hire out, and yet here she was just as jolly and round as an apple. I thought maybe she was an old aunt or something and they took this way of keeping her, so I said, still very polite, "I see you just moved in today?"

"Yes," she said, not really telling me much.

"The family's name is West?"

"Yes."

"You might be Mrs. West's mother?"

"No."

"An aunt, possibly?"

"No."

"Not related at all?"

"No."

"You're just the maid?" I thought afterward that she might not like it mentioned, but once it was out I couldn't take it back.

"Yes." She answered pleasant enough, I will say that for her.

"The work is hard, I expect?"

"No."

"Just the two of them to care for?"

"Yes."

"I'd say you wouldn't like it much."

"It's not bad," she said. "I use magic a lot, of course."

"Magic?" I said. "Does that get your work done sooner?"

"Indeed it does," she said with not so much as a smile or a wink. "You wouldn't think, would you, that right now I'm down on my hands and knees making dinner for my family?"

"No," I said. "I wouldn't think that."

"See?" she said. "Here's our dinner." And she showed me an

acorn, I swear she did, with a mushroom and a scrap of grass in it.

"It hardly looks like enough to go around," I said, kind of backing away.

She laughed at me, kneeling there on the ground with her acorn, and said, "If there's any left over, I'll bring you a dish; you'll find it wonderfully filling."

"But what about your chicken?" I said; I was well along the path away from her, and I did want to know why she got the chicken if she didn't think they were going to eat it.

"Oh, that," she said. "That's for my cat."

Well, who buys a whole chicken for a cat, that shouldn't have chicken bones anyway? Like I told Jane over the phone as soon as I got home, Mr. Honeywell down at the store ought to refuse to sell it to her or at least make her take something more fitting, like ground meat, even though neither of us believed for a minute that the cat was really going to get the chicken, or that she even had a cat, come to think of it; crazy people will say anything that comes into their heads.

I know for a fact that no one next door ate chicken that night, though; my kitchen window overlooks their dining room if I stand on a chair, and what they ate for dinner was something steaming in a big brown bowl. I had to laugh, thinking about that acorn, because that was just what the bowl looked like—a big acorn. Probably that was what put the notion in her head. And, sure enough, later she brought over a dish of it and left it on my back steps, me not wanting to open the door late at night with a crazy lady outside, and like I told Jane, I certainly wasn't going to eat any outlandish concoction made by a crazy lady. But I kind of stirred it around with the end of a spoon, and it smelled all right. It had mushrooms in it and beans, but I couldn't tell what else, and Jane and I decided that probably we were right in the first time and the chicken was for tomorrow.

I had to promise Jane I'd try to get a look inside to see how they set out that fancy furniture, so next morning I brought back their bowl and marched right up to the front door—mostly around town we go in and out back doors but being as they were new and especially since I wasn't sure how you went about calling when people had a maid, I used the front—and gave a knock. I had gotten up early to make a batch of doughnuts, so I'd have something to put in the bowl when I took it back, so I knew that the people next door were up and about because I saw him leaving for work at seven-thirty. He must have worked in the city, to have to get off so early. Jane thinks he's in an office, because she saw him going toward the depot, and he wasn't running; people who work in offices don't have to get in on the dot, Jane said, although how she would know I couldn't tell you.

It was little Mrs. West who opened the door, and I must say she looked agreeable enough. I thought with the maid to bring her breakfast and all she might still be lying in bed, the way they do, but she was all dressed in a pink house dress and was wide awake. She didn't ask me in right away, so I kind of moved a little toward the door, and then she stepped back and said wouldn't I come in, and I must say, funny as that furniture is, she had it fixed up nice, with green curtains on the windows. I couldn't tell from my house what the pattern was on those curtains, but once I was inside I could see it was a pattern of green leaves kind of woven in, and the rug, which of course I had seen when they brought it in, was green too. Some of those big boxes that went in must have held books, because there were a lot of books all put away in bookcases, and before I had a chance to think I said, "My, you must have worked all night to get everything arranged so quick. I didn't see your lights on, though."

"Mallie did it," she said.

"Mallie being the maid?"

She kind of smiled, and then she said, "She's more like a godmother than a maid, really."

I do hate to seem curious, so I just said, "Mallie must keep herself pretty busy. Yesterday she was out digging your garden."

"Yes." It was hard to learn anything out of these people, with their short answers.

"I brought you some doughnuts," I said.

"Thank you." She put the bowl down on one of those little tables—Jane thinks they must hide the wine, because there wasn't a sight of any such thing that I could see—and then she said, "We'll offer them to the cat."

Well, I can tell you I didn't much care for that. "You must have quite a hungry cat," I said to her.

"Yes," she said. "I don't know what we'd do without him. He's Mallie's cat, of course."

"I haven't seen him," I said. If we were going to talk about cats, I figured I could hold my own, having had one cat or another for a matter of sixty years, although it hardly seemed a sensible subject for two ladies to chat over. Like I told Jane, there was a lot she ought to be wanting to know about the village and the people in it and who to go to for hardware and what not —I know for a fact I've put a dozen people off Tom Harris' hardware store since he charged me seventeen cents for a pound of nails—and I was just the person to set her straight on the town. But she was going on about the cat. "——fond of children," she was saying.

"I expect he's company for Mallie," I said.

"Well, he helps her, you know," she said, and then I began to think maybe she was crazy too.

"And how does the cat help Mallie?"

"With her magic."

"I see," I said, and I started to say good-by fast, figuring to get home to the telephone, because people around the village certainly ought to be hearing about what was going on. But before I could get to the door the maid came out of the kitchen and said good morning to me, real polite, and then the maid said to Mrs. West that she was putting together the curtains for the front bedroom and would Mrs. West like to decide on the pattern? And while I just stood there with my jaw hanging, she held out a handful of cobwebs—and I never did see anyone before or since who was able to hold a cobweb pulled out neat, or anyone who would want to, for that matter—and she had a blue jay's feather and a curl of blue ribbon, and she asked me how I liked her curtains.

Well, that did for me, and I got out of there and ran all the way to Jane's house, and, of course, she never believed me. She walked me home just so she could get a look at the outside of the house, and I will be everlastingly shaken if they hadn't gone and put up curtains in that front bedroom, soft white net with a design of blue that Jane said looked like a blue jay's feather. Jane said they were the prettiest curtains she ever saw, but they gave me the shivers every time I looked at them.

It wasn't two days after that I began finding things. Little things, and even some inside my own house. Once there was a basket of grapes on my back steps, and I swear those grapes were never grown around our village. For one thing, they shone like they were covered with silver dust, and smelled like some foreign perfume. I threw them in the garbage, but I kept a little embroidered handkerchief I found on the table in my front hall, and I've got it still in my dresser drawer.

Once I found a colored thimble on the fence post, and once my cat Samantha, that I've had for eleven years and more, came in wearing a little green collar and spat at me when I took it off. One day I found a leaf basket on my kitchen table filled with hazelnuts, and it made me downright shaking mad to think of someone's coming in and out of my house without so much as asking, and me never seeing them come or go.

Things like that never happened before the crazy people moved into the house next door, and I was telling Mrs. Acton so, down on the corner one morning, when young Mrs. O'Neil came by and told us that when she was in the store with her baby she met Mallie the maid. The baby was crying because he was having a time with his teething, and Mallie gave him a little green candy to bite on. We thought Mrs. O'Neil was crazy herself to let her baby have candy that came from that family and said so, and I told them about the drinking that went on and the furniture getting arranged in the dark and the digging in the garden, and

Mrs. Acton said she certainly hoped they weren't going to think
that just because they had a garden they had any claim to be in
the Garden Club.

Mrs. Acton is president of the Garden Club. Jane says I
ought to be president, if things were done right, on account of
having the oldest garden in town, but Mrs. Acton's husband is
the doctor, and I don't know what people thought he might do to
them when they were sick if Mrs. Acton didn't get to be president. Anyway, you'd think Mrs. Acton had some say about who
got into the Garden Club and who didn't, but I had to admit that
in this case we'd all vote with her, even though Mrs. O'Neil did
tell us the next day that she didn't think the people could be all
crazy, because the baby's tooth came through that night with no
more trouble.

Do you know, all this time that maid came into the store
every day, and every day she bought one chicken. Nothing else.
Jane took to dropping in the store when she saw the maid going
along, and she says the maid never bought but one chicken a day.
Once Jane got her nerve up and said to the maid that they must
be fond of chicken, and the maid looked straight at her and told
her right to her face that they were vegetarians.

"All but the cat, I suppose," Jane said, being pretty nervy
when she gets her nerve up.

"Yes," the maid said, "all but the cat."

We finally decided that he must bring food home from the
city, although why Mr. Honeywell's store wasn't good enough
for them I couldn't tell you. After the baby's tooth was better,
Tom O'Neil took them over a batch of fresh-picked sweet corn,
and they must have liked that, because they sent the baby a furry
blue blanket that was so soft that young Mrs. O'Neil said the
baby never needed another, winter or summer, and after being
so sickly, that baby began to grow and got so healthy you
wouldn't know it was the same one, even though the O'Neils
never should have accepted presents from strangers, not knowing
whether the wool might be clean or not.

Then I found out they were dancing next door. Night after

night after night, dancing. Sometimes I'd lie there awake until ten, eleven o'clock, listening to that heathen music and wishing I could get up the nerve to go over and give them a piece of my mind. It wasn't so much the noise keeping me from sleeping—I will say the music was soft and kind of like a lullaby—but people haven't got any right to live like that. Folks should go to bed at a sensible hour and get up at a sensible hour and spend their days doing good deeds and housework. A wife ought to cook dinner for her husband—and not out of cans from the city, either—and she ought to run over next door sometimes with a home-baked cake to pass the time of day and keep up with the news. And most of all a wife ought to go to the store herself where she can meet her neighbors and not just send the maid.

Every morning I'd go out and find fairy rings on the grass, and anyone around here will tell you that means an early winter, and here next door they hadn't even thought to get in coal. I watched every day for Adams and his truck because I knew for a fact that cellar was empty of coal; all I had to do was lean down a little when I was in my garden and I could see right into the cellar, just as swept and clear as though they planned to treat their guests in there. Jane thought they were the kind who went off on a trip somewhere in the winter, shirking responsibilities for facing the snow with their neighbors. The cellar was all you could see, though. They had those green curtains pulled so tight against the windows that even right up close there wasn't a chink to look through from outside, and them inside dancing away. I do wish I could have nerved myself to go right up to that front door and knock some night.

Now, Mary Corn thought I ought to. "You got a right, Addie," she told me one day in the store. "You got every right in the world to make them quiet down at night. You're the nearest neighbor they got, and it's the right thing to do. Tell them they're making a name for themselves around the village."

Well, I couldn't nerve myself, and that's the gracious truth. Every now and then I'd see little Mrs. West walking in the

garden, or Mallie the maid coming out of the woods with a basket
—gathering acorns, never a doubt of it—but I never so much as
nodded my head at them. Down at the store I had to tell Mary
Corn I couldn't do it. "They're foreigners, that's why," I said.
"Foreigners of some kind. They don't rightly seem to understand
what a person says—it's like they're always answering some other
question you didn't ask."

"If they're foreigners," Dora Powers put in, being at the store
to pick up some sugar to frost a cake, "it stands to reason there's
something wrong to bring them here."

"Well, I won't call on foreigners," Mary said.

"You can't treat them the same as you'd treat regular people,"
I said. "I went inside the house, remember, although not as you
might say to pay a call."

So then I had to tell them all over again about the furniture
and the drinking—and it stands to reason that anyone who dances
all night is going to be drinking too—and my good doughnuts
from my grandmother's recipe going to the cat. And Dora, she
thought they were up to no good in the village. Mary said she
didn't know anyone who was going to call, not being sure they
were proper, and then we had to stop talking because in came
Mallie the maid for her chicken.

You would have thought I was the chairman of a committee
or something, the way Dora and Mary kept nudging me and
winking that I should go over and speak to her, but I wasn't
going to make a fool of myself twice, I can tell you. Finally Dora
saw there was no use pushing me, so she marched over and stood
there until the maid turned around and said, "Good morning."

Dora came right out and said, "There's a lot of people around
this village, miss, would like to know a few things."

"I imagine so," the maid said.

"We'd like to know what you're doing in our village," Dora
said.

"We thought it would be a nice place to live," the maid said.
You could see that Dora was caught up short on that, because

who picks a place to live because it's nice? People live in our village because they were born here; they don't just come.

I guess Dora knew we were all waiting for her, because she took a big breath and asked, "And how long do you plan on staying?"

"Oh," the maid said, "I don't think we'll stay very long, after all."

"Even if they don't stay," Mary said later, "they can do a lot of harm while they're here, setting a bad example for our young folk. Just for instance, I heard that the Harris boy got picked up again by the state police for driving without a license."

"Tom Harris is too gentle on that boy," I said. "A boy like that needs whipping and not people living in a house right in town showing him how to drink and dance all night."

Jane came in right then, and she had heard that all the children in town had taken to dropping by the house next door to bring dandelions and berries from the woods—and from their own father's gardens, too, I'll be bound—and the children were telling around that the cat next door could talk. They said he told them stories.

Well, that just about did for me, you can imagine. Children have too much freedom nowadays anyway, without getting nonsense like that into their heads. We asked Annie Lee when she came into the store, and she thought somebody ought to call the police on them, so it could all be stopped before somebody got hurt. She said, suppose one of those kids got a step too far inside that house—how did we know he'd ever get out again? Well, it wasn't too pleasant a thought, I can tell you, but trust Annie Lee to be always looking on the black side. I don't have much dealing with the children as a rule, once they learned they'd better keep away from my apple trees and my melons, and I can't say I know one from the next, except for the Martin boy I had to call the police on once for stealing a piece of tin from my front yard, but I can't say I relished the notion that that cat had his eyes on them. It's not natural, somehow.

And don't you think it was the very next day that they stole the littlest Acton boy? Not quite three years old, and Mrs. Acton so busy with her Garden Club she let him run along into the woods with his sister, and first thing anyone knew they got him. Jane phoned and told me. She heard from Dora, who had been right in the store when the Acton girl came running in to find her mother and tell her the baby had wandered away in the woods, and Mallie the maid had been digging around not ten feet from where they saw him last. Jane said Mrs. Acton and Dora and Mary Corn and half a dozen others were heading right over to the house next door, and I better get outside fast before I missed something, and if she got there late to let her know everything that happened. I barely got out my own front door when down the street they came, maybe ten or twelve mothers, marching along so mad they never had time to be scared.

"Come on, Addie," Dora said to me. "They've finally done it this time."

I knew Jane would never forgive me if I hung back, so out I went and up the front walk to the house next door. Mrs. Acton was ready to go right up and knock, because she was so mad, but before she had a chance the door opened and there was Mrs. West and the little boy, smiling all over as if nothing had happened.

"Mallie found him in the woods," Mrs. West said, and Mrs. Acton grabbed the boy away from her; you could tell they had been frightening him by the way he started to cry as soon as he got to his own mother. All he would say was "kitty," and that put a chill down our backs, you can imagine.

Mrs. Acton was so mad she could hardly talk, but she did manage to say, "You keep away from my children, you hear me?" And Mrs. West looked surprised.

"Mallie found him in the woods," she said. "We were going to bring him home."

"We can guess how you were going to bring him home," Dora shouted, and then Annie Lee piped up, from well in the back, "Why don't you get out of our town?"

"I guess we will," Mrs. West said. "It's not the way we thought it was going to be."

That was nice, wasn't it? Nothing riles me like people knocking this town, where my grandfather built the first house, and I just spoke up right then and there.

"Foreign ways!" I said. "You're heathen wicked people, with your dancing and your maid, and the sooner you leave this town, the better it's going to be for you. Because I might as well tell you"—and I shook my finger right at her—"that certain people in this town aren't going to put up with your fancy ways much longer, and you would be well advised—very well advised, I say —to pack up your furniture and your curtains and your maid and cat and get out of our town before we put you out."

Jane claims she doesn't think I really said it, but all the others were there and can testify I did—all but Mrs. Acton, who never had a good word to say for anybody.

Anyway, right then we found out they had given the little boy something, trying to buy his affection, because Mrs. Acton pried it out of his hand, and he was crying all the time. When she held it out, it was hard to believe, but of course with them there's nothing too low. It was a little gold-colored apple, all shiny and bright, and Mrs. Acton threw it right at the porch floor, as hard as she could, and that little toy shattered into dust.

"We don't want anything from you," Mrs. Acton said, and as I told Jane afterward, it was terrible to see the look on Mrs. West's face. For a minute she just stood there looking at us. Then she turned and went back inside and shut the door.

Someone wanted to throw rocks through the windows, but, as I told them, destroying private property is a crime and we might better leave violence to the menfolks, so Mrs. Acton took her little boy home, and I went in and called Jane. Poor Jane; the whole thing had gone off so fast she hadn't had time to get her corset on.

I hadn't any more than gotten Jane on the phone when I saw through the hall window that a moving van was right there next door, and the men were starting to carry out that fancy furniture. Jane wasn't surprised when I told her over the phone. "Nobody can get moving that fast," she said. "They were probably planning to slip out with that little boy."

"Or maybe the maid did it with magic," I said, and Jane laughed.

"Listen," she said, "go and see what else is going on—I'll hang on the phone."

There wasn't anything to see, even from my front porch, except the moving van and the furniture coming out; not a sign of Mrs. West or the maid.

"He hasn't come home from the city yet," Jane said. "I can see the street from here. They'll have news for him tonight."

That was how they left. I take a lot of the credit for myself, even though Jane tries to make me mad by saying Mrs. Acton did her share. By that night they were gone, bag and baggage, and Jane and I went over the house next door with a flashlight to see what damage they left behind. There wasn't a thing left in that house—not a chicken bone, not an acorn—except for one blue jay's wing upstairs, and that wasn't worth taking home. Jane put it in the incinerator when we came downstairs.

One more thing. My cat Samantha had kittens. That may not surprise you, but it sure as judgment surprised me and Samantha, her being over eleven years old and well past her kitten days, the old fool. But you would have laughed to see her dancing around like a young lady cat, just as light-footed and as pleased as if she thought she was doing something no cat ever did before; and those kittens troubled me.

Folks don't dare come right out and say anything to me about my kittens, of course, but they do keep on with that silly talk about fairies and leprechauns. And there's no denying that the kittens are bright yellow, with orange eyes, and much bigger than normal kittens have a right to be. Sometimes I see them all watching me when I go around the kitchen, and it gives me a cold finger down my back. Half the children in town are begging for those kittens—"fairy kittens," they're calling them—but there isn't a grownup in town would take one.

Jane says there's something downright uncanny about those kittens, but then Jane would even gossip about cats, and I may never speak to her again in all my life. She won't tell me what folks are saying about my kittens, and gossip is one thing I simply cannot endure.

ROBERT FROST

Love and a Question

A Stranger came to the door at eve,
    And he spoke the bridegroom fair.
He bore a green-white stick in his hand,
    And, for all burden, care.
He asked with the eyes more than the lips
    For shelter for the night,
And he turned and looked at the road afar
    Without a window light.

The bridegroom came forth into the porch
    With 'Let us look at the sky,
And question what of the night to be,
    Stranger, you and I.'
The woodbine leaves littered the yard,
    The woodbine berries were blue,
Autumn, yes, winter was in the wind;
    'Stranger, I wish I knew.'

FROM COMPLETE POEMS OF ROBERT FROST. COPYRIGHT 1934
BY HOLT, RINEHART AND WINSTON, INC. COPYRIGHT © 1962 BY ROBERT
FROST. REPRINTED BY PERMISSION OF HOLT, RINEHART AND WINSTON, INC.

Within, the bride in the dusk alone
    Bent over the open fire,
Her face rose-red with the glowing coal
    And the thought of the heart's desire.
The bridegroom looked at the weary road,
    Yet saw but her within,
And wished her heart in a case of gold
    And pinned with a silver pin.

The bridegroom thought it little to give
    A dole of bread, a purse,
A heartfelt prayer for the poor of God,
    Or for the rich a curse;
But whether or not a man was asked
    To mar the love of two
By harboring woe in the bridal house,
    The bridegroom wished he knew.

BEN AMES WILLIAMS

Sheener

When he was sober the man always insisted that his name was Evans, but in his cups he was accustomed to declare, in a boastful fashion, that his name was not Evans at all. However, he never went farther than this, and since none of us were particularly interested, we were satisfied to call him Evans, or, more often, Bum, for short. He was the second assistant janitor; and whereas, in some establishments, a janitor is a man of power and place, it is not so in a newspaper office. In such institutions, where great men are spoken of irreverently and by their first names, a janitor is a man of no importance. How much less, then, his second assistant. It was never a part of Evans' work, for example, to sweep the floors. There is something lordly in the gesture of the broom. But the janitor's first assistant attended to that; and Evans' regular duties were more humble, not unconnected with such things as cuspidors. There was no man so poor to do him honor; yet he had always a certain loftiness of bearing. He was tall, rather above the average height, with a long, thin, bony face like a horse, and an aristocratic stoop about his neck and shoulders. His hands were slender; he walked in a fashion that you might have called a shuffle, but which might also have been characterized as a walk of indolent assurance. His eyes were wash-blue, and his straggling mustache drooped at the corners.

Sober, he was a silent man, but when he had drunk he was apt to become mysteriously loquacious. And he drank whenever the state of his credit permitted. At such times he spoke of his antecedents in a lordly and condescending fashion which we found amusing. "You call me Evans," he would say. "That does well enough, to be sure. Quite so, and all that. Evans! Hah!" And then he would laugh, in a barking fashion that with his long bony countenance always suggested to me a coughing horse. But when he was pressed for details, the man—though he might be weaving and blinking with liquor—put a seal upon his lips. He said there were certain families in one of the Midland Counties of England who would welcome him home if he chose to go; but he never named them, and he never chose to go, and we put him down for a liar by the book. All of us except Sheener.

Sheener was a Jewish newsboy; that is to say, a representative of the only thoroughbred people in the world. I have known Sheener for a good many years, and he is worth knowing; also, the true tale of his life might have inspired Scheherazade. A book must be made of Sheener some day. For the present, it is enough to say that he had the enterprise which adversity has taught his people; he had the humility which they have learned by enduring insults they were powerless to resent; and he had the courage and the heart which were his ancient heritage. And—the man Evans had captured and enslaved his imagination.

He believed in Evans from the beginning. This may have been through a native credulity which failed to manifest itself in his other dealings with the world. I think it more probable that Evans and his pretensions appealed to the love of romance native to Sheener. I think he enjoyed believing, as we enjoy lending ourselves to the illusion of the theater. Whatever the explanation, a certain alliance developed between the two; a something like friendship. I was one of those who laughed at Sheener's credulity, but he told me, in his energetic fashion, that I was making a mistake.

"You got that guy wrong," he would say. "He ain't always

been a bum. A guy with half an eye can see that. The way he talks, and the way he walks, and all. There's class to him, I'm telling you. Class, bo."

"He walks like a splay-footed walrus, and he talks like a drunken old hound," I told Sheener. "He's got you buffaloed, that's all."

"Pull in your horns; you're coming to a bridge," Sheener warned me. "Don't be a goat all your life. He's a gent; that's what this guy is."

"Then I'm glad I'm a roughneck," I retorted; and Sheener shook his head.

"That's all right," he exclaimed. "That's all right. He ain't had it easy, you know. Scrubbing spittoons is enough to take the polish off any guy. I'm telling you he's there. Forty ways. You'll see, bo. You'll see."

"I'm waiting," I said.

"Keep right on," Sheener advised me. "Keep right on. The old stuff is there. It'll show. Take it from me."

I laughed at him. "If I get you," I said, "you're looking for something along the line of 'Noblesse Oblige.' What?"

"Cut the comedy," he retorted. "I'm telling you, the old class is there. You can't keep a fast horse in a poor man's stable."

"Blood will tell, eh?"

"Take it from me," said Sheener.

It will be perceived that Evans had in Sheener not only a disciple; he had an advocate and a defender. And Sheener in these rôles was not to be despised. I have said he was a newsboy; to put it more accurately, he was in his early twenties, with forty years of experience behind him, and with half the newsboys of the city obeying his commands and worshiping him like a minor god. He had full charge of our city circulation and was quite as important, and twice as valuable to the paper, as any news editor could hope to be. In making a friend of him, Evans had found an ally in the high places; and it became speedily apparent that Sheener proposed to be more than a mere friend in name. For instance, I learned one day that he was drawing Evans' wages for him, and had appointed himself in some sort a steward for the other.

"That guy wouldn't ever save a cent," he told me when I questioned him. "I give him enough to get soused on, and I stick five dollars in the bank for him every week. I made him buy a new suit of clothes with it last week. Say, you wouldn't know him if you run into him in his glad rags."

"How does he like your running his affairs?" I asked.

"Like it?" Sheener echoed. "He don't have to like it. If he tries to pull anything on me, I'll poke the old coot in the eye."

I doubt whether this was actually his method of dominating Evans. It is more likely that he used a diplomacy which occasionally appeared in his dealings with the world. Certainly the arrangement presently collapsed, for Sheener confessed to me that he had given his savings back to Evans. We were minus a second assistant janitor for a week as a consequence, and when Evans tottered back to the office and would have gone to work I told him he was through.

He took it meekly enough, but not Sheener. Sheener came to me with fire in his eye.

"Sa-a-ay," he demanded, "what's coming off here, anyhow? What do you think you're trying to pull?"

I asked him what he was talking about, and he said: "Evans says you've given him the hook."

"That's right," I admitted. "He's through."

"He is not," Sheener told me flatly. "You can't fire that guy."

"Why not?"

"He's got to live, ain't he?"

I answered, somewhat glibly, that I did not see the necessity, but the look that sprang at once into Sheener's eyes made me faintly ashamed of myself, and I went on to urge that Evans was failing to do his work and could deserve no consideration.

"That's all right," Sheener told me. "I didn't hear any kicks that his work wasn't done while he was on this bat."

"Oh, I guess it got done all right. Some one had to do it. We can't pay him for work that some one else does."

"Say, don't try to pull that stuff," Sheener protested. "As long as his work is done, you ain't got any kick. This guy has got to have a job, or he'll go bust, quick. It's all that keeps his feet on the ground. If he didn't think he was earning his living, he'd go on the bum in a minute."

I was somewhat impatient with Sheener's insistence, but I was also interested in this developing situation. "Who's going to do his work, anyhow?" I demanded.

For the first time in our acquaintance I saw Sheener look confused. "That's all right too," he told me. "It don't take any skin off your back, long as it's done."

In the end I surrendered. Evans kept his job; and Sheener—I once caught him in the act, to his vast embarrassment—did the janitor's work when Evans was unfit for duty. Also Sheener loaned him money, small sums that mounted into an interesting total; and furthermore I know that on one occasion Sheener fought for him.

The man Evans went his pompous way, accepting Sheener's homage and protection as a matter of right, and in the course of half a dozen years I left the paper for other work, saw Sheener seldom, and Evans not at all.

About ten o'clock one night in early summer I was wandering somewhat aimlessly through the South End to see what I might see when I encountered Sheener. He was running, and his dark face was twisted with anxiety. When he saw me he stopped with an exclamation of relief, and I asked him what the matter was.

"You remember old Bum Evans?" he asked, and added: "He's sick. I'm looking for a doctor. The old guy is just about all in."

"You mean to say you're still looking out for that old tramp?" I demanded.

"Sure, I am," he said hotly; "that old boy is there. He's got the stuff. Him and me are pals." He was hurrying me along the street toward the office of the doctor he sought. I asked where Evans was. "In my room," he told me. "I found him on the street. Last night. He was crazy. The D. T.'s. I ain't been able to get away from him till now. He's asleep. Wait. Here's where the doc hangs out."

Five minutes later the doctor and Sheener and I were retracing our steps toward Sheener's lodging, and presently we crowded into the small room where Evans lay on Sheener's bed. The man's muddy garments were on the floor; he himself tossed and twisted feverishly under Sheener's blankets. Sheener and the doctor bent over him, while I stood by. Evans waked, under the touch of their hands, and waked to sanity. He was cold sober and desperately sick.

When the doctor had done what could be done and gone on his way, Sheener sat down on the edge of the bed and rubbed the old man's head with a tenderness of which I could not have believed the newsboy capable. Evans' eyes were open; he watched the other, and at last he said huskily:

"I say, you know, I'm a bit knocked up."

Sheener reassured him. "That's all right, bo," he said. "You hit the hay. Sleep's the dose for you. I ain't going away."

Evans moved his head on the pillow, as though he were nodding, "A bit tight, wasn't it, what?" he asked.

"Say," Sheener agreed. "You said something, Bum. I thought you'd kick off, sure."

The old man considered for a little, his lips twitching and shaking. "I say, you know," he murmured at last. "Can't have that. Potter's Field, and all that sort of business. Won't do. Sheener, when I do take the jump, you write home for me. Pass the good word. You'll hear from them."

Sheener said: "Sure I will. Who'll I write to, Bum?"

Evans, I think, was unconscious of my presence. He gave Sheener a name; his name. Also, he told him the name of his lawyer, in one of the Midland cities of England, and added certain instructions . . .

When he had drifted into uneasy sleep Sheener came out into the hall to see me off. I asked him what he meant to do.

"What am I going to do?" he repeated. "I'm going to write this guy's lawyer. Let them send for him. This ain't no place for him."

"You'll have your trouble for your pains," I told him. "The old soak is plain liar; that's all."

Sheener laughed at me. "That's all right, bo," he told me. "I know. This guy's the real cheese. You'll see."

I asked him to let me know if he heard anything, and he said he would. But within a day or two I forgot the matter, and would hardly have remembered it if Sheener had not telephoned me a month later.

"Say, you're a wise guy, ain't you?" he derided when I answered the phone. I admitted it. "I got a letter from that lawyer in England," he told me. "This Evans is the stuff, just like I said. His wife run away with another man, and he went to the devil fifteen years ago. They've been looking for him ever since his son grew up."

"Son?" I asked.

"Son. Sure! Raising wheat out in Canada somewhere. They give me his address. He's made a pile. I'm going to write to him."

"What does Bum say?"

"Him? I ain't told him. I won't till I'm sure the kid's coming after him." He said again that I was a wise guy; and I apologized for my wisdom and asked for a share in what was to come. He promised to keep me posted.

Ten days later he telephoned me while I was at supper to ask if I could come to his room. I said: "What's up?"

"The old guy's boy is coming after him," Sheener said. "He's got the shakes waiting. I want you to come and help me take care of him."

"When's the boy coming?"

"Gets in at midnight to-night," said Sheener.

I promised to make haste; and half an hour later I joined them in Sheener's room. Sheener let me in. Evans himself sat in something like a stupor, on a chair by the bed. He was dressed in a cheap suit of ready-made clothes, to which he lent a certain dignity. His cheeks were shaven clean, his mustache was trimmed, his thin hair was plastered down on his bony skull. The man stared straight before him, trembling and quivering. He did not look toward me when I came in; and Sheener and I sat down by the table and talked together in undertones.

"The boy's really coming?" I asked.

Sheener said proudly: "I'm telling you."

"You heard from him?"

"Got a wire the day he got my letter."

"You've told Bum?"

"I told him right away. I had to do it. The old boy was sober by then, and crazy for a shot of booze. That was Monday. He wanted to go out and get pied; but when I told him about his boy, he began to cry. And he ain't touched a drop since then."

"You haven't let him?"

"Sure I'd let him. But he wouldn't. I always told you the class was there. He says to me: 'I can't let my boy see me in this state, you know. Have to straighten up a bit. I'll need new clothes.' "

"I noticed his new suit."

"Sure," Sheener agreed. "I bought it for him."

"Out of his savings?"

"He ain't been saving much lately."

"Sheener," I asked, "how much does he owe you? For money loaned and spent for him."

Sheener said hotly: "He don't owe me a cent."

"I know. But how much have you spent on him?"

"If I hadn't give it to him, I'd have blowed it somehow. He needed it."

I guessed at a hundred dollars, at two hundred. Sheener would not tell me. "I'm telling you, he's my pal," he said. "I'm not looking for anything out of this."

"If this millionaire son of his has any decency, he'll make it up to you."

"He don't know a thing about me," said Sheener, "except my name. I've just wrote as though I knowed the old guy, here in the house, see. Said he was sick, and all."

"And the boy gets in to-night."

"Midnight," said Sheener, and Evans, from his chair, echoed: "Midnight!" Then asked with a certain stiff anxiety: "Do I look all right, Sheener? Look all right to see my boy?"

"Say," Sheener told him. "You look like the Prince of Wales." He went across to where the other sat and gripped him by the shoulder. "You look like the king o' the world."

Old Evans brushed at his coat anxiously; his fingers picked and twisted; and Sheener sat down on the bed beside him and began to soothe and comfort the man as though he were a child.

The son was to arrive by way of Montreal, and at eleven o'clock we left Sheener's room for the station. There was a flower stand on the corner, and Sheener bought a red carnation and fixed it in the old man's buttonhole. "That's the way the boy'll know him," he told me. "They ain't seen each other for—since the boy was a kid."

Evans accepted the attention querulously; he was trembling and feeble, yet held his head high. We took the subway, reached the station, sat down for a space in the waiting room.

But Evans was impatient; he wanted to be out in the train shed, and we went out there and walked up and down before the gate. I noticed that he was studying Sheener with some embarrassment in his eyes. Sheener was, of course, an unprepossessing figure. Lean, swarthy, somewhat flashy of dress, he looked what he was. He was my friend, of course, and I was able to look beneath the exterior. But it seemed to me that sight of him distressed Evans.

In the end the old man said, somewhat furtively: "I say, you know, I want to meet my boy alone. You won't mind standing back a bit when the train comes in."

"Sure," Sheener told him. "We won't get in the way. You'll see. He'll pick you out in a minute, old man. Leave it to me."

Evans nodded. "Quite so," he said with some relief. "Quite so, to be sure."

So we waited. Waited till the train slid in at the end of the long train shed. Sheener gripped the old man's arm. "There he comes," he said sharply. "Take a brace, now. Stand right there, where he'll spot you when he comes out. Right there, bo."

"You'll step back a bit, eh, what?" Evans asked.

"Don't worry about us," Sheener told him. "Just you keep your eye skinned for the boy. Good luck, bo."

We left him standing there, a tall, gaunt, shaky figure. Sheener and I drew back toward the stairs that lead to the elevated structure, and watched from that vantage point. The train stopped, and the passengers came into the station, at first in a trickle and then in a stream, with porters hurrying before them, baggage-laden.

The son was one of the first. He emerged from the gate, a tall chap, not unlike his father. Stopped for a moment, casting his eyes about, and saw the flower in the old man's lapel. Leaped toward him hungrily.

They gripped hands, and we saw the son drop his hand on the father's shoulder. They stood there, hands still clasped, while the young man's porter waited in the background. We could hear the son's eager questions, hear the older man's drawled replies. Saw them turn at last, and heard the young man say: "Taxi!" The porter caught up the bag. The taxi stand was at our left, and they came almost directly toward us.

As they approached, Sheener stepped forward, a cheap, somewhat disruptable, figure. His hand was extended toward the younger man. The son saw him, looked at him in some surprise, looked toward his father inquiringly.

Evans saw Sheener too, and a red flush crept up his gaunt cheeks. He did not pause, did not take Sheener's extended hand; instead he looked the newsboy through and through.

Sheener fell back to my side. They stalked past us, out to the taxi stand.

I moved forward. I would have halted them, but Sheener caught my arm. I said hotly: "But see here. He can't throw you like that."

Sheener brushed his sleeve across his eyes. "Hell," he said huskily. "A gent like him can't let on he knows a guy like me."

I looked at Sheener, and I forgot old Evans and his son. I looked at Sheener, and I caught his elbow and we turned away.

He had been quite right, of course, all the time. Blood will always tell. You can't keep a fast horse in a poor man's stable. And a man is always a man, in any guise.

If you still doubt, do as I did. Consider Sheener.

F. K. FRANKLIN

Nigger Horse

The August day began sleepily. By eight o'clock, the sun was already hot, and humidity hung like a thick blanket of steam across the pine forests and drought-stricken fields of western Louisiana. Highway 171, a cracked and beaten ribbon of concrete stretching south of Many toward Lake Charles and the Gulf, lay comparatively quiet beneath the quickening glare. An hour earlier, empty log trucks, coming north with slack chains clanking on their bouncing trailers, had met and passed empty oil trucks booming southward to the refineries of Lake Charles. Soldiers, living in whatever they could rent along the highway, had long since gone down to Fort Polk, and there were no school buses to take up the slack between the other men coming to town to their jobs and the housewives driving in later to the stores.

Mrs. Findley led her daughter's small dun horse around the corner of the house. Stooping, she tied his halter rope into the swivel of the picket pin she'd screwed into the baked ground the day before. "There's not much to eat, old fellow," she murmured, straightening to survey the sparse lawn, aware in a kind of passive relief of the transitory peace on the highway. The horse lowered his head, blew dust with his soft breath, then drew back his lips to nibble at the seared grass with the edges of his teeth.

Mrs. Findley sighed and stretched a little, thinking of her second cup of coffee warming on the stove. For the next hour or more, the shade of the tulip tree would be across the back porch. The breeze rising from the meadows would still hold the night's coolness. I'll put out the crayons and paper, she thought; the children can draw while I drink my coffee. It's going to be another breathless, blazing day.

She sighed again. Her gaze wandered, following the white ribbon of the highway to its vanishing point among the green-gold cottonwoods that separated the piney forests from the cow pastures that ringed the town. Dreamily she raised her hand to push back the short bangs clinging damply to her tanned forehead. The gesture brought a sense of life to her languid body and a momentary pleasure. To be young was the great thing. To be young . . . And regretfully she remembered that Cart wouldn't be home for another five nights.

"One more damn battalion exercise to test what we learned on the first one," he'd said. "I think myself it's a general's nightmare put to practice. God, I tell you, Katty, love, it's hot out there in those woods!"

Poor Cart . . . Well . . .

With a last glance for the knot she'd tied on the picket ring—knot-tying being with her an uncertain skill—she turned back toward the house, just in time to see her year-old toddler pivot near the edge of the raised and unrailed carport as he gravely mimicked the whirling dance of his five-year-old sister.

"Mikey!" She ran toward him, mentally hearing the thud of his small, defenseless head against concrete and the anguished wail that would follow, but imagined disaster and her own abrupt movement were suddenly and bewilderingly effaced by the whine of overheated rubber, the squeal of brakes, the blare of a horn, and a frantic drumbeat of hooves upon pavement.

The horse!

She swung around wildly, sure that he'd broken from a careless knot to run to certain doom upon the highway, but he was where she'd left him, his small head raised, ears pricked, compact body swinging on his haunches to face the racket just beyond the hedge screening the edge of the lawn. A great bay horse came pounding down the center of the highway. Black mane and tail flying, head up, he veered in terror as brakes shrieked again, a horn blared its raucous cry, and an empty oil truck clattered around him. Trumpeting his panic, the horse galloped past, and Mrs. Findley saw his eyes roll wild with fear. Suddenly he wheeled, steel shoes sliding, air grunting from his big barrel. For a second he hesitated, head high, snorting, then came charging diagonally back across the highway to slide down the steep embankment onto the Findley's lawn, where he made a wide circle around the excited dun, who, whirling to meet him, threw the weight of his body against the picket rope with audible stress.

The scene remained frozen. The horses stood nose to nose blowing in soft recognition of their kinship; the highway was once more empty; the two children remained mute and round-eyed at the edge of the carport; Katherine Findley, still entranced by the tranquility of the hour and the image of a second cup of coffee, stood rooted in surprise and confusion—until the moment exploded as a large van truck applied air brakes for the long curve and hill toward town. Sssssssst! The bay whirled back on his haunches, terror renewed, while the dun, caught up in the contagion of his fear, lunged forward, teeth bared. The creak of his strained tether shook loose the vestiges of Mrs. Findley's morning dream.

She ran back toward the horse, sure that at any moment he would break away to join the bay now rushing down the lawn toward the highway again. She grabbed the picket rope, heaving her weight against that of the plunging dun, and somehow won enough slack to get the knot untied, the rope free of the pin. Her fingers rubbed raw, she half pulled, half ran with the excited horse toward the corner of the house and the fenced lot beyond.

"Watch Mikey!" she screamed over her shoulder, but was drowned out by a sudden melee of trumpeting animals, for the bay, seeing them go, had swung from the highway to come racing after them. Neighing shrilly, he circled them with long-

legged bounds that set the dun to wheeling and lunging. In the
confusion Mrs. Findley heard the baby's distant wail, but she
could not stop. On she plunged, half pulled, half directing the
dun toward the safety of the lot. As they raced through the open
gate the big bay shot in behind them to circle the fence with ringing bugle calls, his long legs skimming the dusty ground, his lean
body stretched, neck extended, head turning this way and that.
With her last ounce of strength, Mrs. Findley jerked rope and
halter from the excited dun, then jumped back as he tore off in
the stranger's erratic wake. Affected by each other's terror, the
two horses dashed around the lot, charging in close upon each
other, the bay with his bounding strides, the dun belly close to
the ground, short legs driving.

My God, they'll go through the fence! she thought, a little
frightened and wholly awed by their unleashed power. Mesmer-
ized, she stood and watched them careen around and around the
dusty lot, gradually exchanging panic for pleasure. They began
to buck and lash out at each other with teeth and heels. At the far
corner of the lot, they wheeled, reared, feinted at each other's
quarters, then broke away in a drumming gallop again. Their
intoxication was infectious, and in spite of the heat Mrs. Findley
felt, herself, a powerful urge to run and leap. God, I used to run
and run, she thought, remembering the feel of cool damp earth
beneath her bare feet as she ran down a rustling lane of corn-
stalks, or the feel of grass cropped smooth and close as velvet
down the pasture slope, or the soft dust of the road and the small
clouds she sent puffing from under her racing sneakers. I ran, she
thought. I ran and ran, and I'm glad I still remember the feeling.

"Mommie!"

Dimly she heard the baby's howls and the older child calling.
Ah now . . . ah now, and she turned, running, to the shed where
she filled the oat can quickly and banged it hard against the door
until the dun slowed, turning his head in her direction. He came
to an abrupt, stiff-legged halt, then ambled over.

"Chowhound!" she said to him, scattering the oats in the big
washtub under the cottonwood that was shedding its fuzzy bark

like a winter coat into the dust. "And lucky for me that you are," she added, for the bay was still making his rushes along the fence. As she fastened the gate behind her, she saw him come to a halt finally, then turn toward the shed, puzzled. He nickered softly and started toward the dun at an easy, swinging trot, his ears pricked, nostrils widening to the scent of the sweet grain. She couldn't wait, though, and tense with awareness of her deserted children, she ran toward the house.

"Ah, Mikey, Mikey, what's the matter?" She gathered the toddler against her breasts and swept the two children into the house. "Did he fall, Jeannie? Are you hurt, honey?"

"No, he didn't fall or anything. He's just kind of scared. He thought the horses ran over you, I guess." Jeannie wrinkled her golden round brow in disdain.

"Well, there's nothing to be afraid of. Somebody just lost their horse, and isn't that an odd thing to lose?" She brushed the little boy's forelock back from his damp forehead and was acutely conscious of the yearning of love she willed through her fingers. As though a touch could make safe, she thought. Or hold back terror.

Jeannie giggled. "How could anybody lose a horse, Mommie?"

She looked up and smiled into the wide blue eyes. "I don't know, but he certainly looks lost."

"Can I go see it, Mommie? Can I?"

"Yes, after awhile. We'll all go down, but right now let's let the poor fellow calm down. He got pretty frightened out there on the road with all those trucks. I wonder how on earth I go about finding . . ." Through the screen door, she saw an elderly car slide to a stop before the mailbox. Oh, maybe the mailman would know. "Run out on the back porch, Jeannie, and get your crayons," she said. Swinging the baby to her hip, she hurried through the front door and up the drive, calling, "Mr. Enders! Oh, Mr. Enders!"

He waited, and, panting, she bent to talk through the open window, the sun like fire upon her back, the baby dragging at her arm. He nodded wisely at her question and considered. Old, dry-boned, his every movement so slow it seemed a series of separated jerks, he fumbled forth a letter for her.

"Yep. Saw that horse, I reckon. Saw him back toward town maybe half an hour ago. Like to have got hisself killed. Big truck dern near run him down. Nope, don't have any idea in the world who owns him. Ganted like he is, reckon he's a nigger horse. That there's all you got today, Missus Carter." He added the last in a tone that took some satisfaction in the meagerness of her mail. With a vague jerk of bony fingers, he let out the clutch and moved slowly away as she stepped back on the highway shoulder.

Nigger horse? What did that mean?

Sticking the letter between her teeth, she juggled the baby to a firmer seat over her left hip, then moved slowly down the drive. One hand freed, she turned the letter over. Damn! Someone had opened it. Across the stained front "MISSENT" was scrawled in pencil and the flap, rudely torn, had been pasted back down with a ragged piece of scotch tape. Irritation shook her. Four times in one month! Couldn't that old man read? Surely there wasn't another Major and Mrs. Carter Findley on Route 1, Many, Louisiana! And, she thought, touched by surprise, we've lived here almost a year!

She stared at the ugly, penciled word, her privacy invaded. Who was this mysterious reader of their mail, this presumptous person who tore open their letters so crudely and so crudely tossed them back? In anger she visualized a fat woman in a shapeless dress stained down the front, a regular country woman obsessed with the private life of her neighbors, so meager was her own. Why woman, though? she wondered, stopping short in the drive. Why not some dried-out husk of a man given to spending his days on his front porch the better to watch the comings and going of his neighbors? No, the woman was there to stay, fat, not wholly clean, with a broad moon face and narrow lips pursed in perpetual disapproval. Pale, freckled skin, thin hair, pale eyes . . .

Ugh! She almost dropped the letter in revulsion. Really, this time I'll put in a complaint at the Post Office. I should have done it long ago!

"Hey, there, boy," she murmured aloud as Mikey nuzzled his warm face and cool, button nose into her neck. She put him down in the drive and bent over him in the sun as he immediately squatted to explore a bright pebble with chubby fingers. No, she thought with an uneasy mental shrug, I can't make trouble for that old man. I suppose it's enough to be working at all at his age and frail as he seems. Perhaps, as they say, if someone took his job away he'd lie down and die. Vaguely, she felt that she'd stepped close to cruelty, that she'd been indulging in a certain city-bred smugness. What a struggle it was to be tolerant, especially for a Yankee before what seemed so much nonsense in southern ways.

She patted Mikey's cropped head and stopped to catch one small hand. "Come on, chum, or you and I'll come down with sunstroke."

"Hey, lady!"

She straightened and turned, startled, bringing Mikey to his feet. Except for the occasional passing car or truck, she'd felt herself alone in the hot, bright morning, but there was a man not ten feet away at the head of the drive grinning amiably, his reddened eyes bold. He was almost as old as the mail carrier, but where the years had withered the carrier's flesh they had bloated the body of this man, encasing his large bones in yellowing fat. Soiled khaki pants, beltless, strained to meet a filthy white shirt over the protuberance of his belly. A greasy stetson, wide brim curled on each side, sat far back on his sweating head.

"Seen you catch that there horse, lady," he drawled, moving down the drive toward her, his gaze roaming her bare brown legs with relish. He bent to touch Mikey under the chin. The small boy clutched Mrs. Findley's leg, trying to hide behind her sunburned calf. Hastily she stuck her letter in the back pocket of her shorts and stooped to lift him again into her arms.

"Seen you from yonder," the man continued unperturbed. "Waiting for a ride to Lake Charles and seen that truck all but hit the critter. Ain't yours, is he?"

"No. Oh no. I don't know whose . . ." She shook her head helplessly. Where on earth had he been standing that she hadn't seen him? She glanced along the highway, deserted now except for the distant glitter of an oncoming car. The skin along her backbone prickled. Strange people and so much she didn't understand about them . . . Sometimes, no, often, she felt a sense of threat, a kind of obscure violence. Especially when she answered the reiterated question, "Where you from, Missus?" and then watched the cold suspicion move into their eyes. "Up North, eh?"

"Keep the Negro thing out of your talk, honey," Cart had warned her. "It's like waving a bloody shirt at a bull. Oh, sure, if you get pinned down, tell 'em you think this race thing is all wrong, but don't go looking for trouble. You'd not have far to look, I'm afraid."

For his sake, and hers too, because they had to live here and she did not want to live afraid, she'd ridden herd upon her inclination to protest, to denounce; yet even so, there was still suspicion, half-smothered, and her own sense of unspoken threat. Why? She wasn't altogether sure.

"Naw, never laid eyes on that one before. Ain't a bad-lookin' animal, huh? Skinny as all get out, but he's got real classy action, don't he?" the man was saying, his gaze wandering from her face to her legs and back again.

"Yes. He's too good a horse to be running up and down the highway like that. I wonder what I ought to do." Mikey was heavy in her arms. She shifted him to her other hip. "I don't have any idea how to go about finding his owner. I don't know many people in town, and then my husband . . ." She stopped, letting it drift away, remembering her isolation in this house from week-end to week-end, and Cart's stern instructions never to mention to anyone that he was gone so much.

"It gives me the heeby-jeebies to think someone might notice that I'm not around," he said. "If it weren't for the damn battalion hours, I could at least get back a couple of nights a week."

"I've the dog and the pistol," she'd reminded him. "Who needs you?" Often, though, in the dark hours she'd not found it so merry to be alone with two small children with the nearest neighbor out of sight across a meadow and beyond a small wood. Drunken voices sometimes sounded on the highway and hitch-hikers shouted curses after the cars that did not stop. Sometimes obscene cries sprayed the night and whiskey bottles clattered on the gravel shoulder. One night she'd been awakened by the frantic barking of the dog and the sound of someone moving about on the carport, but the dog's fierce yapping had sent whoever it was back into the night. After that, when the dog was aroused, she prowled the house, the loaded pistol in her hand, all the dire stories of rape and murder she'd ever read crowding her courage.

"Whyn't you call Rod Jones?" the old man suggested lazily. "Being town marshal like he is, chances are he'd know all about that horse. Or, anyways, figure something to do with him. And when it comes to liking horses, he don't take second place to nobody in this here parish!

"Rod Jones? Oh, thank you." Relieved, she shifted the baby once more and started down the drive. That rheumy, red stare upon her bare legs made her flesh creep.

" 'Course, if it's some nigger horse, likely he can't help you none," he called after her.

She nodded and went on thoughtfully to the house. Nigger horse? There it was again. Once inside the house, she carefully latched the screen door and deposited Mikey with his sister amid the reams of paper and the crayons, broken and whole, on the back porch. She poured her long-delayed second mug of coffee and went to stand by the back door. In the lot, the two horses were standing quietly now, head to head, in the shade of the shed. Nigger horse, whatever it meant. Funny that they never said whiteman's horse, or whiteman's shack. Coffee mug in hand, she turned and went back through the kitchen to the hall and here searched through the thin phone directory until she found Jones, Rod. What must it be like to be characterized in one great lump like that, she mused, listening to the dial tone change to an intermittent buzzing. Two rings, two rings, two rings . . . It's all part and parcel of forbidding a natural human dignity. It's akin to never addressing them as Mr. or Mrs. or Miss. But why do people . . . ?

"Jones speaking."

The drawling voice stopped abruptly, leaving silence in her ear. Confused, she gasped and rushed into the breach. "Oh, Mr. Jones, this is Mrs. Findley, Mrs. Carter Findley out on the Lake Charles highway. I was told that perhaps you could help me . . ." She went on to explain, too effusively, too incoherently, with no sound from him on the other end of the wire. Good grief, she thought, when she had finished, is he there? She cleared her throat. "Ah, Mr. . . . ?" but the slow voice cut in lazily, "Bay, you say, Ma'am? Seventeen hands or more, huh? Big fellow, ain't he? I reckon, though, it's a new one for me. Wasn't sweated much, you say? Can't have come far then. Nope, can't think whose horse it might be, less it belongs to some nigger close in to town. Tell you what, Missus Findley, if anybody calls wanting word of a lost horse, I'll send 'em right on over to your place, okay? You can keep him in your lot awhile, can't you? Good. If don't nobody claim him by nightfall, why then I'll come over and fetch him to the Fairground and get him outten your way. You just give me another buzz around five o'clock, okay? Fine." His voice was friendly, reassuring. It came over the line to her like a fatherly pat on the shoulder.

She hung up bemused. There might be a thousand people up and down the highway and in the town of Many itself, and among them perhaps forty horses and mules, most of which she already knew on sight, for she, like Marshal Jones, had a fondness for horses, and she would run to the window at the first clatter of hoof on highway to watch the cow pony or walking horse go by. Like a child, she thought. Just like a child. Still, they had a fascination. There was the thin, white walker whose rider favored black—black stetson, black shirt, black pants, black boots —and sang nasal cowboy laments at the top of his voice as he paced through town. There was the old brown plow horse that came by every Saturday morning with two boys on his broad and sagging back. The only Negro she'd seen with horses was an old, very dark man, bent and worn, who drove a rail-thin team, always with a plow in the wagonbed and a woman, his wife she'd presumed, as white as herself, sitting erect with a painful dignity on the seat beside him. She'd spent many an unquiet moment wondering about this couple.

If this was a . . . if this horse did belong to a Negro, might he have had to keep him hidden because he was so plainly a good horse, far too classy for a Negro to own?

Oh Lord, she thought, would they begrudge him even this?

Still, she held back, knowing herself prone to find this thing, knowing she'd brought it with her to the deep South, that she'd come with her Yankee mind convinced of the evil, the bigotry, the cruelty of this land. That was a year ago, though, she thought, and now I'm only confused. Oh, there was no honor to the South in the dingy café entrances marked colored that opened from dismal, trash-laden alleys; the waiting rooms, Colored, always dirty, shabby, hopelessly overcrowded; the separate and inferior sections of movie theaters; the branded ads in phone directories and newspapers; the long unpainted and unrepaired firetraps that were the Negro schools; and last and perhaps worst, the one-room shacks and tiny shotgun houses with yards that served as gardens, chicken pens, cow lots, child's play yard, family privy, and dump with everywhere, inside and out, the smell of poverty, humility, indignity.

No honor, no honor here for any race or religion; little enough compassion for a man, a woman, or a child if the skin was black . . . yet, she'd found no human fiends, no country dolts, no southern Jukes. In the cold light of honesty she would have to admit that these people, their neighbors, had treated her and Cart with great friendliness, great generosity. Everyone they'd had dealings with had been unfailingly courteous, eager to help the strangers in their midst, eager to oblige, quick to stop with a word and a smile. Why is it they aren't collapsed by guilt? she wondered. Are they perhaps like pit donkeys that are slowly blinded in their daily darkness until they forget the sun?

"It isn't easy to be righteous any more," she said aloud and walked to the front door to stare out at the glittering morning.

"We go back to the Bible for our way of life," Mrs. Justin Bayard, their neighbor across the meadow, had told her once, and it was the first time anyone had mentioned the subject to her though they'd been in Many almost half a year. "It's Noah's curse on the seed of Ham because he dared to laugh, he dared to think evil of his father. Their skin and their souls will be black until God chooses to lift that curse, you know. Until then it is destined that they must be set apart. Oh yes," she said softly, smiling upon her visitor, her face still pretty though weathered in soft wrinkles, "all this was decreed a long time ago."

"Oh?" Mrs. Findley had murmured, bewildered.

"That's why, you see," Mrs. Bayard went on calmly, fluffing out her graying hair. "If the Church should ever reinterpret the Bible, why then, I suppose we might . . . well, there would be change. Justin says there might have to be . . ."

But I didn't even bring it up, Katherine Findley thought. I only mentioned that in Pennsylvania we'd not have green grass and flowers so early. Do I touch a nerve every time?

Her relief had been great when Mrs. Bayard suddenly clapped her hands and raised her soft voice in a shrill cry toward the clink of china and silverware in the kitchen. "Nancy! Bring Missus Findley coffee, hear?" then went on to describe the beauty of azalea gardens in New Orleans. She neither interrupted herself nor glanced up when a large sullen Negro woman, neat and clean, came slip-slopping into the room to set a heavy silver tray of coffee things before her, then, relieved of the burden, grunted and turned her white sneakers, slit to accommodate every bunion and corn, toward the kitchen.

"Oh my!" Mrs. Bayard had looked after her then, sighing lightly. "Do you take cream or sugar, my dear? If you do, I'm afraid she's forgotten . . ."

"No, I really prefer it black," Mrs. Findley had replied hastily.

Louisiana coffee, dark and bitter.

Somewhere in the back of the house a thin voice had wavered like a slice of bright sky in a broken puddle. "Here chick, chick, chicky! Come chick, chick chicky!"

"My mother," Mrs. Bayard had explained, rising. "She's eighty-two and her blood pressure is very high. On some days even the tranquilizers don't help very much. Will you excuse me?"

"Of course."

When Mrs. Bayard returned, her smile was both affectionate and rueful. "Poor Mamma, it worries her so that she hasn't fed the chickens or that maybe we aren't all in for the night. There were nine of us, you see, and when her blood pressure's up she calls us all night by name wanting to know if we're home and the doors are locked. She must go back thirty years in time, poor thing, to do all her fretting over again. It's a little strange sometimes to hear her call, because my oldest brother died years ago and one of my sisters passed away just last fall . . . She had a hard life, Mama did."

And Mrs. Findley had left remembering the wry affection and the morose Negro woman who carried the curse of Ham's children on her shoulders. How do you make anything of that? Where was evil clear-cut and defined? Mrs. Bayard who'd sent Nancy over to care for the children during the siege of doctor's treatments for her infected chigger bites, or Mrs. Wilson across the road who showered them with washed, crisp produce from her garden, or Mr. Hainey at the store who was kindness itself when she ran short of funds the month Cart was gone to Texas on a prolonged maneuver . . . how could she find evil among them? And yet . . . wouldn't they, all of them, deny a Negro dreamer his dream of being a knight of sorts mounted upon a big bay charger? Wouldn't they call him biggety for riding a free-walking horse, a gaited horse?

God knows, she thought, the pride-saving dreams of such dreamers are sometimes manifested in bizarre and childish ways —old cars streaked with clashing colors and loaded down with cheap chrome ornaments, unnecessary lights and mirrors and horns, raccoon tails flapping from every jutting surface; gaudy parasols and costume jewelry; bright, sleazy dresses or shirts— all like this horse, impractical and bankrupting. A man can buttress a meager livelihood with a mule, but this horse can only eat. He's far too high-strung, too leggy for wagon or plow. A silly thing to own. A Negro dreamer must surely know . . .

Oh, she told herself sternly, I've work to do!

Slowly, the shade retreated from the house. The children grew hot and fretful as the sun invaded every corner. Mrs. Findley moved more and more lethargically about her tasks, washing both dishes and clothes, dusting a little, sweeping, trying to entertain the restless children, bedding Mikey at last for his nap and settling Jeannie before the phonograph with a stack of her favorite records. She returned to the kitchen to give thought to supper, but, worn by the heat, went instead to stand in the doorway, hoping against hope that a wandering breeze would drift out of the late afternoon. Nothing stirred. Not a leaf, not a long weed, not even a fly. In the dusty lot, the two horses stood motionless, head to head, in the shade of the cottonwoods.

Can I survive the summer? she wondered, then saw abruptly that the dreamer had arrived. He came, a bridle in his hand, in a group of four Negro men who walked diffidently along the hedge, skirting the edge of the lawn. Irresolutely, she moved across the porch and opened the screen door to call across the yard, "Are you looking for a horse?"

They halted, clumping. All four turned their heads toward her, and she was not even sure which one replied, "Yes, Ma'am, we's looking for a hoss."

Hurrying down the steps, she moved toward them. "He came

down the highway this morning. Oh, quite early. It's really a miracle he wasn't hit by a truck or a car. He saw my horse. I had him staked out front, you know, and he saw him and came into the yard. He followed me into the lot when I took my horse in and I didn't know what to do. I didn't know how to find out whose . . . then someone told me to call the Marshal, Marshal Jones, and he . . . I suppose he told you where he was." Disconcerted, she paused, conscious that she was chattering, painfully conscious of their impassive stares and wanting only to be easy and natural, wanting them to be easy and natural in return and hating with all her heart the whine of apology she heard in her voice. Nervously, she stopped to pick a piece of paper from the ground.

"Yes, Ma'am. Can we get him outten there now?"

"Oh, yes, yes, of course. Just go on through the gate. Here, I'll help. I'll keep my horse back. They've gotten kind of chummy." Ah, Lord, why this shrillness, this overemphasis, why anything at all?

They waited, letting her precede them into the lot, their faces unchanging. Once inside, though, the dreamer moved away from his companions toward the horse. "Heah, Big Boy, heah, son. C'mon now, hear?"

"He's an awfully fine horse!" Mrs. Findley exclaimed, over-riding that soft entreaty. "He's certainly a good-looking animal!"

No one spoke. They merely glanced sideways at her from the corners of their eyes. Young men, all in their early twenties, they were dressed as though they'd come straight from their work. Their faded overalls were sweaty and stained, their T-shirts dusty. Cutting trees, she thought, or working at the lumber mill.

"He got on fine with our horse," she went on compulsively. "They've been playing like . . . a couple of kids. You know, running and kicking up. I fed them . . . him. I hope you don't mind . . . ?"

"No, Ma'am."

Again, whose murmur?

"Heah, Big Boy," the dreamer said, extending his hand palm up. Recognition pricking his ears, the bay turned his head, then came lazily toward him. The dun followed, loath to lose his new friend.

"Hey, Big Boy. Hey Now." The bay stretched his long, slender neck to nibble and blow softly into the open hand. Man and horse stood a moment, then the man moved the reins over the thin neck and slipped the bit swiftly between the even teeth. He turned and led the bay from the lot. His mute companions followed. Mrs. Findley had her hands full keeping back the disappointed dun and getting the gate closed between the two animals. By the time she had it fastened, the men and horse were halfway to the highway. Defeated, she moved slowly off at a tangent toward the house. Nigger horse! she thought, watching the bay's long, springy strides, the arch of his neck. Ah, my God, it isn't my fault! It isn't the way I feel! Can't they tell? Can't they understand that I didn't do this to them, that I never would? Never! I cannot help that my skin is white . . .

Startled, she caught herself up. How many times must they have said that to themselves—I cannot help that my skin is . . . Ah, how terrible and how stupid! All one's life, for no reason . . .

Aching for forgiveness, for absolution, she raised her head and saw that the men had stopped at the edge of the highway, still closely clumped, the horse a part of that clump now. The dreamer had half turned back, the reins in his hand. Oh, she thought, stabbed anew, he's certain to think I'll tell. He'll be sure I'll destroy his dream. And she hurried toward them, crying, "I won't mention . . . I'll not tell the Marshal whose horse . . ."

The others turned back also, then exchanged glances.

I'll promise, she thought desperately, still hurrying toward them. He must understand that I'm not one of them, that I'll not help them. He must not be allowed to worry . . .

"I won't say you came. I'll not tell them. It'll be quite all right . . ."

They stared at her blankly.

Sweating, panting a little, she heard herself babbling and faltered, overcome by futility. I can't ever climb that wall, she thought sadly. I can't even find the words. I've tried. And I've only made myself ridiculous . . .

But unable to give up, she cried, "I like horses. I . . . I hate to see them . . . suffer just because . . . when it's not fair. . . ."

Three of the men laughed harshly, turned their backs, and walked on out upon the highway. The dreamer paused a moment more. "Thank you, Ma'am, for catching him up. I'm obliged," he called across the intervening space, his gaze direct.

She smiled, vastly relieved, for it seemed to her that his voice was normal, even sincere, and that their eyes met upon a human plane. Then he cleared his throat, spat toward her into the grass, and turned to run after his friends, the bay trotting gracefully behind him.

D. H. LAWRENCE

The Rocking-Horse Winner

There was a woman who was beautiful, who started with all the advantages, yet she had no luck. She married for love, and the love turned to dust. She had bonny children, yet she felt they had been thrust upon her, and she could not love them. They looked at her coldly, as if they were finding fault with her. And hurriedly she felt she must cover up some fault in herself. Yet what it was that she must cover up she never knew. Nevertheless, when her children were present, she always felt the centre of her heart go hard. This troubled her, and in her manner she was all the more gentle and anxious for her children, as if she loved them very much. Only she herself knew that at the centre of her heart was a hard little place that could not feel love, no, not for anybody. Everybody else said of her: "She is such a good mother. She adores her children." Only she herself, and her children themselves, knew it was not so. They read it in each other's eyes.

There were a boy and two little girls. They lived in a pleasant house, with a garden, and they had discreet servants and felt themselves superior to anyone in the neighborhood. Although they lived in style, they felt always an anxiety in the house. There was never enough money. The mother had a small income, and the father had a small income, but not nearly enough for the social position which they had to keep up. The father went into town to some office. But though he had good prospects, these prospects never materialized. There was always the grinding sense of the shortage of money, though the style was always kept up.

At last the mother said: "I will see if I can't make something." But she did not know where to begin. She racked her brains, and tried this thing and the other, but could not find anything successful. The failure made deep lines come into her face. Her children were growing up, they would have to go to school. There must be more money, there must be more money. The father, who was always very handsome and expensive in his tastes, seemed as if he never would be able to do anything worth doing. And the mother, who had a great belief in herself, did not succeed any better, and her tastes were just as expensive.

And so the house came to be haunted by the unspoken phrase: There must be more money! There must be more money! The children could hear it all the time, though nobody said it aloud. They heard it at Christmas, when the expensive and splendid toys filled the nursery. Behind the shining modern rocking-horse, behind the smart doll's-house, a voice would start whispering: "There must be more money! There must be more money!" And the children would stop playing, to listen for a moment. They would look into each other's eyes, to see if they had all heard. And each one saw in the eyes of the other two that they too had heard. "There must be more money! There must be more money!"

It came whispering from the springs of the still-swaying rocking-horse, and even the horse, bending his wooden, champing head, heard it. The big doll, sitting so pink and smirking in her new pram, could hear it quite plainly, and seemed to be smirking all the more self-consciously because of it. The foolish puppy, too, that took the place of the teddy-bear, he was looking so extraordinarily foolish for no other reason but that he heard the secret whisper all over the house: "There must be more money!"

Yet nobody ever said it aloud. The whisper was everywhere, and therefore no one spoke it. Just as no one ever says: "We are breathing!" in spite of the fact that breath is coming and going all the time.

"Mother," said the boy Paul one day, "why don't we keep a car of our own? Why do we always use uncle's, or else a taxi?"

"Because we're the poor members of the family," said the mother.

"But why are we, mother?"

"Well—I suppose," she said slowly and bitterly, "it's because your father has no luck."

The boy was silent for some time.

"Is luck money, mother?" he asked, rather timidly.

"No, Paul. Not quite. It's what causes you to have money."

"Oh!" said Paul vaguely. "I thought when Uncle Oscar said filthy lucker, it meant money."

"Filthy lucre does mean money," said the mother. "But it's lucre, not luck."

"Oh!" said the boy. "Then what is luck, mother?"

"It's what causes you to have money. If you're lucky you have money. That's why it's better to be born lucky than rich. If you're rich, you may lose your money. But if you're lucky, you will always get more money."

"Oh! Will you? And is father not lucky?"

"Very unlucky, I should say," she said bitterly.

The boy watched her with unsure eyes.

"Why?" he asked.

"I don't know. Nobody ever knows why one person is lucky and another unlucky."

"Don't they? Nobody at all? Does nobody know?"

"Perhaps God. But he never tells."

"He ought to, then. And aren't you lucky either, mother?"

"I can't be, if I married an unlucky husband."

"But by yourself, aren't you?"

"I used to think I was, before I married. Now I think I am very unlucky indeed."

"Why?"

"Well—never mind! Perhaps I'm not really," she said.

The child looked at her, to see if she meant it. But he saw by the lines of her mouth, that she was only trying to hide something from him.

"Well, anyhow," he said stoutly, "I'm a lucky person."

"Why?" said his mother, with a sudden laugh.

He stared at her. He didn't even know why he had said it.

"God told me," he asserted, brazening it out.

"I hope He did, dear!" she said, again with a laugh, but rather bitter.

"He did, mother!"

"Excellent!" said the mother, using one of her husband's exclamations.

The boy saw she did not believe him; or, rather, that she paid no attention to his assertion. This angered him somewhat, and made him want to compel her attention.

He went off by himself, vaguely, in a childish way, seeking for the clue to "luck." Absorbed, taking no heed of other people, he went about with a sort of stealth, seeking inwardly for luck. He wanted luck, he wanted it, he wanted it. When the two girls were playing dolls in the nursery, he would sit on his big rocking-horse, charging madly into space, with a frenzy that made the little girls peer at him uneasily. Wildly the horse careered, the waving dark hair of the boy tossed, his eyes had a strange glare in them. The little girls dared not speak to him.

When he had ridden to the end of his mad little journey, he climbed down and stood in front of his rocking-horse, staring fixedly into its lowered face. Its red mouth was slightly open, its big eye was wide and glassy-bright.

"Now!" he would silently command the snorting steed. "Now, take me to where there is luck! Now take me!"

And he would slash the horse on the neck with the little whip he had asked Uncle Oscar for. He knew the horse could take him to where there was luck, if only he forced it. So he would mount again, and start his furious ride, hoping at last to get there. He knew he could get there.

"You'll break your horse, Paul!" said the nurse.

"He's always riding like that! I wish he'd leave off!" said his elder sister Joan.

But he only glared down on them in silence. Nurse gave him up. She could make nothing of him. Anyhow he was growing beyond her.

One day his mother and his Uncle Oscar came in when he was on one of his furious rides. He did not speak to them.

"Hallo, you young jockey! Riding a winner?" said his uncle.

"Aren't you growing too big for a rocking-horse? You're not a very little boy any longer, you know," said his mother.

But Paul only gave a blue glare from his big, rather close-set eyes. He would speak to nobody when he was in full tilt. His mother watched him with an anxious expression on her face.

At last he suddenly stopped forcing his horse into the mechanical gallop, and slid down.

"Well, I got there!" he announced fiercely, his blue eyes still flaring, and his sturdy long legs straddling apart.

"Where did you get to?" asked his mother.

"Where I wanted to go," he flared back at her.

"That's right, son!" said Uncle Oscar. "Don't you stop till you get there. What's the horse's name?"

"He doesn't have a name," said the boy.

"Gets on without all right?" asked the uncle.

"Well, he has different names. He was called Sansovino last week."

"Sansovino, eh? Won the Ascot. How did you know his name?"

"He always talks about horse-races with Bassett," said Joan.

The uncle was delighted to find that his small nephew was posted with all the racing news. Bassett, the young gardener, who had been wounded in the left foot in the war and had got his present job through Oscar Cresswell, whose batman he had been, was a perfect blade of the "turf." He lived in the racing events, and the small boy lived with him.

Oscar Cresswell got it all from Bassett.

"Master Paul comes and asks me, so I can't do more than tell him, sir," said Basset, his face terribly serious, as if he were speaking of religious matters.

"And does he ever put anything on a horse he fancies?"

"Well—I don't want to give him away—he's a young sport, a fine sport, sir. Would you mind asking him yourself? He sort of takes a pleasure in it, and perhaps he'd feel I was giving him away, sir, if you don't mind."

Bassett was serious as a church.

The uncle went back to his nephew, and took him off for a ride in the car.

"Say, Paul, old man, do you ever put anything on a horse?" the uncle asked.

The boy watched the handsome man closely.

"Why, do you think I oughn't to?" he parried.

"Not a bit of it! I thought perhaps you might give me a tip for the Lincoln."

The car sped on into the country, going down to Uncle Oscar's place in Hampshire.

"Honour bright?" said the nephew.

"Honour bright, son!" said the uncle.

"Well, then, Daffodil."

"Daffodil! I doubt it, sonny. What about Mirza?"

"I only know the winner," said the boy. "That's Daffodil."

"Daffodil, eh?"

There was a pause. Daffodil was an obscure horse comparatively.

"Uncle!"

"Yes, son?"

"You won't let it go any further, will you? I promised
Bassett."

"Bassett be damned, old man! What's he got to do with it?"

"We're partners. We've been partners from the first. Uncle,
he lent me my first five shillings, which I lost. I promised him,
honour bright, it was only between me and him; only you gave
me that ten-shilling note I started winning with, so I thought
you were lucky. You won't let it go any further, will you?"

The boy gazed at his uncle from those big, hot, blue eyes,
set rather close together. The uncle stirred and laughed uneasily.

"Right you are, son! I'll keep your tip private. Daffodil, eh?
How much are you putting on him?"

"All except twenty pounds," said the boy. "I keep that in
reserve."

The uncle thought it a good joke.

"You keep twenty pounds in reserve, do you, you young
romancer? What are you betting, then?"

"I'm betting three hundred," said the boy gravely. "But
it's between you and me, Uncle Oscar! Honour bright?"

The uncle burst into a roar of laughter.

"It's between you and me all right, you young Nat Gould,"
he said, laughing. "But where's your three hundred?"

"Bassett keeps it for me. We're partners."

"You are, are you! And what is Bassett putting on Daffodil?"

"He won't go quite as high as I do, I expect. Perhaps he'll go
a hundred and fifty."

"What, pennies?" laughed the uncle.

"Pounds," said the child, with a surprised look at his uncle.
"Bassett keeps a bigger reserve than I do."

Between wonder and amusement Uncle Oscar was silent. He
pursued the matter no further, but he determined to take his
nephew with him to the Lincoln races.

"Now, son," he said, "I'm putting twenty on Mirza, and I'll
put five for you on any horse you fancy. What's your pick?"

"Daffodil, uncle."

"No, not the fiver on Daffodil!"

"I should if it was my own fiver," said the child.

"Good! Good! Right you are! A fiver for me and a fiver for you on Daffodil."

The child had never been to a race-meeting before, and his eyes were blue fire. He pursed his mouth tight, and watched. A Frenchman just in front had put his money on Lancelot. Wild with excitement, he flayed his arms up and down, yelling "Lancelot! Lancelot!" in his French accent.

Daffodil came in first, Lancelot second, Mirza third. The child, flushed and with eyes blazing, was curiously serene. His uncle brought him four five-pound notes, four to one.

"What am I to do with these?" he cried, waving them before the boy's eyes.

"I suppose we'll talk to Bassett," said the boy. "I expect I have fifteen hundred now; and twenty in reserve; and this twenty."

His uncle studied him for some moments.

"Look here, son!" he said. "You're not serious about Bassett and that fifteen hundred, are you?"

"Yes, I am. But it's between you and me, uncle. Honour bright!"

"Honour bright all right, son! But I must talk to Bassett."

"If you'd like to be a partner, uncle, with Bassett and me, we could all be partners. Only, you'd have to promise, honour bright, uncle, not to let it go beyond us three. Bassett and I are lucky, and you must be lucky, because it was your ten shillings I started winning with. . . ."

Uncle Oscar took both Bassett and Paul into Richmond Park for an afternoon, and there they talked.

"It's like this, you see, sir," Bassett said. "Master Paul would get me talking about racing events, spinning yarns, you know, sir. And he was always keen on knowing if I'd made or if I'd lost. It's about a year since, now, and I put five shillings on Blush of Dawn for him—and we lost. Then the luck turned, with that ten shillings he had from you, that we put on Singhalese. And since that time, it's been pretty steady, all things considering. What do you say, Master Paul?"

"We're all right when we're sure," said Paul. "It's when we're not quite sure that we go down."

"Oh, but we're careful then," said Bassett.

"But when are you sure?" smiled Uncle Oscar.

"It's Master Paul, sir," said Bassett, in a secret, religious voice. "It's as if he had it from heaven. Like Daffodil, now, for the Lincoln. That was as sure as eggs."

"Did you put anything on Daffodil?" asked Oscar Cresswell.

"Yes, sir, I made my bit."

"And my nephew?"

Bassett was obstinately silent, looking at Paul.

"I made twelve hundred, didn't I, Bassett? I told uncle I was putting three hundred on Daffodil."

"That's right," said Bassett, nodding.

"But where's the money?" asked the uncle.

"I keep it safe locked up, sir. Master Paul he can have it any minute he likes to ask for it."

"What, fifteen hundred pounds?"

"And twenty! And forty, that is, with the twenty he made on the course."

"It's amazing!" said the uncle.

"If Master Paul offers you to be partners, sir, I would, if I were you; if you'll excuse me," said Bassett.

Oscar Cresswell thought about it.

"I'll see the money," he said.

They drove home again, and sure enough, Bassett came round to the garden-house with fifteen hundred pounds in notes. The twenty pounds reserve was left with Joe Glee, in the Turf Commission deposit.

"You see, it's all right, uncle, when I'm sure! Then we go strong, for all we're worth. Don't we, Bassett?"

"We do that, Master Paul."

"And when are you sure?" said the uncle, laughing.

"Oh, well, sometimes I'm absolutely sure, like about Daffodil," said the boy; "and sometimes I have an idea; and sometimes I haven't even an idea, have I, Bassett? Then we're careful, because we mostly go down."

"You do, do you! And when you're sure, like about Daffodil, what makes you sure, sonny?"

"Oh, well, I don't know," said the boy uneasily. "I'm sure, you know, uncle; that's all."

"It's as if he had it from heaven, sir," Bassett reiterated.

"I should say so!" said the uncle.

But he became a partner. And when the Leger was coming on, Paul was "sure" about Lively Spark, which was a quite inconsiderable horse. The boy insisted on putting a thousand on the horse, Bassett went for five hundred, and Oscar Cresswell two hundred. Lively Spark came in first, and the betting had been ten to one against him. Paul had made ten thousand.

"You see," he said, "I was absolutely sure of him."

Even Oscar Cresswell had cleared two thousand.

"Look here, son," he said, "this sort of thing makes me nervous."

"It needn't uncle! Perhaps I shan't be sure again for a long time."

"But what are you going to do with your money?" asked the uncle.

"Of course," said the boy, "I started it for mother. She said she had no luck, because father is unlucky, so I thought if I was lucky, it might stop whispering."

"What might stop whispering?"

"Our house. I hate our house for whispering."

"What does it whisper?"

"Why—why"—the boy fidgeted—"why, I don't know. But it's always short of money, you know, uncle."

"I know it, son, I know it."

"You know people send mother writs, don't you, uncle?"

"I'm afraid I do," said the uncle.

"And then the house whispers, like people laughing at you behind your back. It's awful, that is! I thought if I was lucky . . ."

"You might stop it," added the uncle.

The boy watched him with big blue eyes that had an uncanny cold fire in them, and he said never a word.

"Well, then!" said the uncle. "What are we doing?"

"I shouldn't like mother to know I was lucky," said the boy.

"Why not, son?"

"She'd stop me."

"I don't think she would."

"Oh!"—and the boy writhed in an odd way—"I don't want her to know, uncle."

"All right, son! We'll manage it without her knowing."

They managed it very easily. Paul, at the other's suggestion, handed over five thousand pounds to his uncle, who deposited it with the family lawyer, who was then to inform Paul's mother that a relative had put five thousand pounds into his hands, which sum was to be paid out a thousand pounds at a time, on the mother's birthday, for the next five years.

"So she'll have a birthday present of a thousand pounds for five successive years," said Uncle Oscar. "I hope it won't make it all the harder for her later."

Paul's mother had her birthday in November. The house had been "whispering" worse than ever lately, and, even in spite of his luck, Paul could not bear up against it. He was very anxious to see the effect of the birthday letter, telling his mother about the thousand pounds.

When there were no visitors, Paul now took his meals with his parents, as he was beyond the nursery control. His mother went into town nearly every day. She had discovered that she had an odd knack of sketching furs and dress materials, so she worked secretly in the studio of a friend who was the chief "artist" for the leading drapers. She drew the figures of ladies in furs and ladies in silk and sequins for the newspaper advertisements. This young woman artist earned several thousand pounds a year, but Paul's mother only made several hundreds, and she was again dissatisfied. She so wanted to be first in something, and she did not succeed, even in making sketches for drapery advertisements.

She was down to breakfast on the morning of her birthday. Paul watched her face as she read her letters. He knew the lawyer's letter. As his mother read it, her face hardened and became more expressionless. Then a cold determined look came on her mouth. She hid the letter under the pile of others, and said not a word about it.

"Didn't you have anything nice in the post for your birthday, mother?" said Paul.

"Quite moderately nice," she said, her voice cold and absent.

She went away to town without saying more.

But in the afternoon Uncle Oscar appeared. He said Paul's mother had had a long interview with the lawyer, asking if the whole five thousand could be advanced at once, as she was in debt.

"What do you think, uncle?" said the boy.

"I leave it to you, son."

"Oh, let her have it, then! We can get some more with the other," said the boy.

"A bird in the hand is worth two in the bush, laddie!" said Uncle Oscar.

"But I'm sure to know for the Grand National; or the Lincolnshire; or else the Derby. I'm sure to know for one of them," said Paul.

So Uncle Oscar signed the agreement, and Paul's mother touched the whole five thousand. Then something very curious happened. The voices in the house suddenly went mad, like a chorus of frogs on a spring evening. There were certain new furnishings, and Paul had a tutor. He was really going to Eton, his father's school, in the following autumn. There were flowers in the winter, and a blossoming of the luxury Paul's mother had been used to. And yet the voices in the house, behind the sprays of mimosa and almond blossom, and from under the piles of iridescent cushions, simply trilled and screamed in a sort of ecstasy: "There must be more money! Oh-h-h, there must be more money. Oh, now now-w! Now-w-w—there must be more money!—more than ever! More than ever!"

It frightened Paul terribly. He studied away at his Latin and Greek with his tutor. But his intense hours were spent with Bassett. The Grand National had gone by: he had not "known," and had lost a hundred pounds. Summer was at hand. He was in agony for the Lincoln. But even for the Lincoln he didn't "know" and he lost fifty pounds. He became wild-eyed and strange, as if something were going to explode in him.

"Let it alone, son! Don't you bother about it!" urged Uncle Oscar. But it was as if the boy couldn't really hear what his uncle was saying.

"I've got to know for the Derby! I've got to know for the Derby!" the child reiterated, his big blue eyes blazing with a sort of madness.

His mother noticed how overwrought he was.

"You'd better go to the seaside. Wouldn't you like to go now to the seaside, instead of waiting? I think you'd better," she said, looking down at him anxiously, her heart curiously heavy because of him.

But the child lifted his uncanny blue eyes.

"I couldn't possibly go before the Derby, mother!" he said. "I couldn't possibly!"

"Why not?" she said, her voice becoming heavy when she was opposed. "Why not? You can still go from the seaside to see the Derby with your Uncle Oscar, if that's what you wish. No need for you to wait here. Besides, I think you care too much about these races. It's a bad sign. My family has been a gambling family, and you won't know till you grow up how much damage it has done. But it has done damage. I shall have to send Bassett away, and ask Uncle Oscar not to talk racing to you, unless you promise to be reasonable about it; go away to the seaside and forget it. You're all nerves!"

"I'll do what you like, mother, so long as you don't send me away till after the Derby," the boy said.

"Send you away from where? Just from this house?"

"Yes," he said, gazing at her.

"Why, you curious child, what makes you care about this house so much, suddenly? I never knew you loved it."

He gazed at her without speaking. He had a secret within a secret, something he had not divulged, even to Bassett or to his Uncle Oscar.

But his mother, after standing undecided and a little bit sullen for some moments, said:

"Very well, then! Don't go to the seaside till after the Derby, if you don't wish it. But promise me you won't let your nerves go to pieces. Promise you won't think so much about horse-racing and events, as you call them!"

"Oh, no," said the boy casually. "I won't think much about them, mother. You needn't worry. I wouldn't worry, mother, if I were you."

"If you were me and I were you," said his mother, "I wonder what we should do!"

"But you know you needn't worry, mother, don't you?" the boy repeated.

"I should be awfully glad to know it," she said wearily.

"Oh, well, you can, you know. I mean, you ought to know you needn't worry," he insisted.

"Ought I? Then I'll see about it," she said.

Paul's secret of secrets was his wooden horse, that which had no name. Since he was emancipated from a nurse and a nursery-governess, he had had his rocking-horse removed to his own bed-room at the top of the house.

"Surely, you're too big for a rocking-horse!" his mother had remonstrated.

"Well, you see, mother, till I can have a real horse, I like to have some sort of animal about," had been his quaint answer.

"Do you feel he keeps you company?" she laughed.

"Oh, yes! He's very good, he always keeps me company, when I'm there," said Paul.

So the horse, rather shabby, stood in an arrested prance in the boy's bedroom.

The Derby was drawing near, and the boy grew more and more tense. He hardly heard what was spoken to him, he was very frail, and his eyes were really uncanny. His mother had sudden seizures of uneasiness about him. Sometimes, for half-an-hour, she would feel a sudden anxiety about him that was almost anguish. She wanted to rush to him at once, and know he was safe.

Two nights before the Derby, she was at a big party in town, when one of her rushes of anxiety about her boy, her first-born, gripped her heart till she could hardly speak. She fought with the feeling, might and main, for she believed in common sense. But it was too strong. She had to leave the dance and go downstairs to telephone to the country. The children's nursery-governess was terribly surprised and startled at being rung up in the night.

"Are the children all right, Miss Wilmont?"

"Oh yes, they are quite all right."

"Master Paul? Is he all right?"

"He went to bed as right as a trivet. Shall I run up and look at him?"

"No," said Paul's mother reluctantly. "No! Don't trouble. It's all right. Don't sit up. We shall be home fairly soon." She did not want her son's privacy intruded upon.

"Very good," said the governess.

It was about one o'clock when Paul's mother and father drove up to their house. All was still. Paul's mother went to her room and slipped off her white fur cloak. She had told her maid not to wait up for her. She heard her husband downstairs, mixing a whisky-and-soda.

And then, because of the strange anxiety at her heart, she stole upstairs to her son's room. Noiselessly she went along the upper corridor. Was there a faint noise? What was it?

She stood, with arrested muscles, outside his door, listening. There was a strange, heavy, and yet not loud noise. Her heart stood still. It was a soundless noise, yet rushing and powerful. Something huge, in violent, hushed motion. What was it? What in God's name was it? She ought to know. She felt that she knew the noise. She knew what it was.

Yet she could not place it. She couldn't say what it was. And on and on it went, like a madness.

Softly, frozen with anxiety and fear, she turned the door-handle.

The room was dark. Yet in the space near the window, she heard and saw something plunging to and fro. She gazed in fear and amazement.

Then suddenly she switched on the light, and saw her son, in his green pajamas, madly surging on the rocking-horse. The blaze of light suddenly lit him up, as he urged the wooden horse, and lit her up, as she stood, blonde, in her dress of pale green and crystal, in the doorway.

"Paul!" she cried. "Whatever are you doing?"

"It's Malabar!" he screamed, in a powerful, strange voice. "It's Malabar."

His eyes blazed at her for one strange and senseless second, as he ceased urging his wooden horse. Then he fell with a crash to the ground, and she, all her tormented motherhood flooding upon her, rushed to gather him up.

But he was unconscious, and unconscious he remained, with some brain-fever. He talked and tossed, and his mother sat stonily by his side.

"Malabar! It's Malabar! Bassett, Bassett, I know! It's Malabar!"

So the child cried, trying to get up and urge the rocking-horse that gave him his inspiration.

"What does he mean by Malabar?" asked the heart-frozen mother.

"I don't know," said the father stonily.

"What does he mean by Malabar?" she asked her brother Oscar.

"It's one of the horses running for the Derby," was the answer.

And, in spite of himself, Oscar Cresswell spoke to Bassett, and himself put a thousand on Malabar: at fourteen to one.

The third day of the illness was critical: they were waiting for a change. The boy, with his rather long, curly hair, was tossing ceaselessly on the pillow. He neither slept nor regained consciousness, and his eyes were like blue stones. His mother sat, feeling her heart had gone, turned actually into a stone.

In the evening, Oscar Cresswell did not come, but Bassett sent a message, saying could he come up for one moment, just one moment? Paul's mother was very angry at the intrusion, but on second thought she agreed. The boy was the same. Perhaps Bassett might bring him to consciousness.

The gardener, a shortish fellow with a little brown mustache, and sharp little brown eyes, tiptoed into the room, touched his imaginary cap to Paul's mother, and stole to the bedside, staring with glittering, smallish eyes, at the tossing, dying child.

"Master Paul!" he whispered. "Master Paul! Malabar come in first all right, a clean win. I did as you told me. You've made over seventy thousand pounds, you have; you've got over eighty thousand. Malabar came in all right, Master Paul."

"Malabar! Malabar! Did I say Malabar, mother? Did I say Malabar? Do you think I'm lucky, mother? I knew Malabar, didn't I? Over eighty thousand pounds! I call that lucky, don't you, mother? Over eighty thousand pounds! I knew, didn't I know I knew? Malabar came in all right. If I ride my horse till I'm sure, then I tell you, Bassett, you can go as high as you like. Did you go for all you were worth, Bassett?"

"I went a thousand on it, Master Paul."

"I never told you, mother, that if I can ride my horse, and get there, then I'm absolutely sure—oh, absolutely! Mother, did I ever tell you? I am lucky."

"No, you never did," said the mother.

But the boy died in the night.

And even as he lay dead, his mother heard her brother's voice saying to her: "My God, Hester, you're eighty-odd thousand to the good and a poor devil of a son to the bad. But, poor devil, poor devil, he's best gone out of a life where he rides his rocking-horse to find a winner."

ALEX GABY

Fifty-two Miles to Terror

There was a little, persistent ache in his right shoulder, as there always was now when he was behind the wheel for more than an hour or two, but that was all. Everything else was fine.

Another three hours at this rate, and they would be at Mildred's. That would make it after eleven; the children would all be too tired for roughhouse, and by twelve just the grown-ups, he, Paula, Mildred and Frank—— They would all have a drink and talk a little, laugh a little; have a nice, quiet good time.

He shifted his weight and the ache went out for a second, like a candle snuffed, but was back again. He changed position, hunched against his door.

"Shoulder bothering you some, dear?" Paula looked at him, the excitement of the trip lifting the corners of her mouth.

He glanced at her and back to the long, straight road. "Same as always. Nothing to worry about, hon."

"Let me rub it, dad. You want me to?" Ruth, in the back seat, hunched forward and began to knead his shoulder. He saw her earnest, ten-year-old face in the rear-view mirror, her dark hair wind-blown, frizzled astride her head like a maniacal mop. Her eyes were intense, staring down at his shoulder, and the intensity puckered her mouth while her strong little hands kneaded his shoulder. Doing a good job of it too.

"Ruth, please," Paula said quietly. "You know you shouldn't bother your father when he's driving. The way people drive these days, it's bad enough, without all that tugging and pulling."

Ruth stopped the kneading and sat back in her seat. "Gee, how much longer, dad?" she asked. "I can't wait to see Aunt Mildred and the kids and everything. You know?"

"We'll be in Crockerville in a few minutes," he said. "Then only a hundred and twenty miles to Waco."

Paula leaned closer to him. "Getting tired, dear? Three hours against that sun, I wonder you're not blind. And, Biff, slow it down a little, will you?"

He glanced down at the speedometer. Fifty-five. Speed creeps up on you on these long, straight stretches, he thought. But that's Texas—long, straight stretches. "Paula, I'm only doing a little over fifty. Relax. No one more careful behind a wheel than I is—I am—I is. I like 'I is' better."

" 'I is' is right," she laughed, and leaned close to him, nuzzling her nose against his cheek.

He looked down and noticed that her face was as shiny as marbles, reddened with the heat and the dust that came in with the wind through her window, loosening her hair, but lovely as always—lovely to him.

He stole a quick look in the rear-view mirror at Ruth, and saw her in profile, gazing out her window, whistling something horrible between her teeth, and for one piercing instant he felt sorry for her, alone, while he and Paula—

The sign for Crockerville came at them, and he slowed down to thirty miles per hour. DON'T HURRY TO KILL OUR CHILDREN. POPULATION 2196. WE WANT TO KEEP IT THAT WAY! the sign said.

In the center of Crockerville, at the only major intersection in the town, there was a light. It was red, and he stopped. A car pulled up on his right with a squeal of brakes. Glancing across to the car, he saw that it was red—incredibly red—with all the chrome removed, and the whole body lowered so that it nestled over its wheels like a short-legged bug.

"Hot-rod," he said, nodding toward the red car. "More and more of them around."

Paula looked at it and wrinkled her nose. "It looks like some kind of a throwback. A hybrid or something. Why do they do that to perfectly good cars?"

He shrugged. "They soup them up to really go. Me, I'll take Steady Nelly here."

"I like Steady Nelly too," Ruth piped up from the back seat. "I'll bet we could beat that old thing, couldn't we, dad?"

Paula whipped her head around to glare at Ruth. "You can just make up your mind, young lady, we're not going to try!" she snapped. "That's just the kind of thing you read about, all this racing on the highways!"

He laughed and hunched over the wheel. He tapped the accelerator and gunned the motor several times.

She turned on him. "Biff! What's wrong with both of you? You're not going to race that idiotic thing!" No matter how many times he threatened to do something spectacular in the car—and never did—she always reacted. It was a private little joke with him.

The light changed. "Watch this!" he hissed through clenched teeth. "That underslung meat wagon, we'll take 'em!"

He stepped down hard on the accelerator and the car lurched ahead. Suddenly there was a peculiar, staccato snort on his right, and the red car was up to him, inching past him, and they were racing. There was a car parked in the path of the red car, not two hundred feet ahead, with people getting out of it at the curb, but the snorting grew louder and the red car did not slow down. A hundred feet, less than a hundred feet, so close now that he stamped his foot on the brake and twisted hard to the left on his wheel, just time enough so that the red car whipped between him and the car parked at the curb, roaring with the staccato bursts down the street. *They knew I'd do that. They knew it.*

He was terribly angry and yanked the car back into the right lane.

"Did you see that?" Paula gasped. "Biff, did you see that? Those people—they might have been killed!"

"I saw it," he said. "Blamed fools. I'd like to knock their heads together. They knew I'd pull out, Paula. The blamed fools knew I would. Can you tie that?"

"You could have beat 'em, dad," Ruth said contentedly from the back seat, her excitement subsiding. "You just didn't want to, with me and mommy in the car."

They stopped on the main street and had soda and a hot dog at a curbside stand, and when they started again, it was getting quite dark, with the sun finally extinguished against the flat edge of the land. He settled back in his seat and made himself comfortable, not quite so happy as he had been before the red car; angry with the red car for knowing he would pull out. They were near the edge of town now, with the main street becoming road again, and there were the signs up at the gas stations: LAST CHANCE, FILL 'ER UP. NEXT GAS STATION 60 MILES.

There was the red car, sitting like a sleek worm on the apron of the last gas station on the edge of town on his right, glowing with the color of bright blood under the arc lights of the station. The driver had a soft-drink bottle in his hand, hanging out the window, his arm limp, as if the bottle were unbearably heavy.

Without the slightest hesitation, Biff pulled off the road and slid to a stop near the red car. He could see their white shirts gleaming inside the low coupé.

"Hey, you, in there," he said sharply. "If you want to break your necks, go to it! But just your own necks, see? If you can't drive that jalopy properly, stay off the road! You hear me?" He was yelling so loud that it surprised him.

Ruth was hopping up and down in the back, also yelling. "We could beat you any day, so there! Nya-a-a-a-nya-a-a-a-a!"

"Biff . . . Ruth! Stop it!" Paula was pushing at his shoulder.

He subsided and started the car moving. Suddenly there was a laugh from the red car, clear and sharp, and a piercing rebel yell—the kind you hear at Western movies or in pictures about the Civil War.

They drove on, and now the darkness came in completely to scoop away the land on either side of the road, and all he could see of the road itself was the part in his headlights, skimming into him easily, smoothly. He relaxed, switched on his far beams, and loosened his grip on the wheel, yearning to be at Mildred's. He sighed and stepped on the gas a little too hard.

"Biff, slow down a little," Paula said and closed her window. The wind had chilled quickly as the darkness came.

"Sure, hon," he said, and glanced in the mirror at Ruth in the back seat. She was already asleep.

There had been no car besides his on the road. It was the old road, and everyone else used the new superhighway about ten miles north. But this road was a little shorter, and he knew it well. He wished there were a few cars on the road. It would be a friendly thing to do—dipping headlights to an oncoming car, sort of a friendly bow.

And then the red car drew up behind him. First there had been a glow in his rear-view mirror, and then there was the red car. He knew it was that car because its headlights were so low, hugging the road. A cold finger touched his spine, and he glanced quickly at Paula; she was dozing, and for that he was suddenly grateful.

He speeded up a little and the lights of the red car receded, but then drew up again behind him, making him feel that it was about to crawl up his neck, like some monster insect.

For at least ten minutes more the red car followed him so closely that if he stepped on his brakes, it would ram him, but he knew they were sure he would not do that, just as they were sure back there in Crockerville that he would yank his wheel to the left so that they could careen in between him and the car at the curb.

He thought how foolish it had been to stop at that gasoline station to yell at them that way. He should have remembered it

was Saturday night; not much for people in places like Crockerville, on a by-passed road, to do on Saturday nights, and when a
couple of them have one of those souped-up jalopies—— He shook
his head and made up his mind to stop worrying about the red
car. Sooner or later it would turn around and go back; he'd be
hanged if he'd speed up more than the sixty he was doing. Let
them eat his dust if they wanted it that way, but all the time he
knew it would not stay that way, not for long. This was not what
they wanted.

It came quickly. There was that peculiar sputtering snort
behind him, and suddenly it was beside him. He could have
reached out his hand and touched it, but in another instant it was
in front of him, staying just a few feet in front. Then he smelled
the exhaust fumes coming in through his air vents. The smell
grew quickly very strong.

Paula was awake. "What was that?" she said, shaking her
head sharply. "Oh, Biff! That car—what's he doing here? When
——" Her hand flew to her throat, and when he saw that, besides
everything else he felt, he could feel the anger rising in him too.

"Relax, honey," he said quietly, his voice tight with the effort
to sound normal. "You'll wake Ruth. They just want to play a
little, but I'm not having any. They'll get tired of playing games
in a little while, and then they'll go back. Just take it easy."

In a few minutes the red car began to slow down, and he was
forced to use his brakes several times to keep from riding up their
two inadequate little bumpers. Finally they were going thirty
miles an hour. His hands clenched, impatience battling with the
anger in him, anger not quite covering the cold finger on his
spine.

"What do they want?" Paula asked wildly.

He tried to grin at her. "They're getting even for that hiding
I gave them back there. It's nothing. They'll quit soon, Paula.
Just relax, now." *They've got to quit.*

"I tried to stop you back there," she said. "You and Ruth,
yammering away at them—those—— Biff! What does he want?"

She had seen the driver of the red car put his arm out of his window and motion them forward, an indolent, graceful movement of the white-shirted arm, inviting them ahead.

The coldness went out of his spine. Now he knew what they wanted, and the knowledge was a relief softening his grip on the wheel. "They wanted to race, honey, that's all," he said. "We'll give them their little race, and that will be that. Really got under their skin back in Crockerville. These hot-rodders have a certain kind of pride."

"Biff, don't race them!" she gasped. "It's dangerous!"

"It's more dangerous not to," he said. "They're going to have their little race or else. Well, here goes."

"Biff!"

He stepped hard on the accelerator, drew out abreast of the red car, and then put the accelerator all the way down to the floor. The car leaped ahead and for an instant it seemed he would pass them. He threw a quick sideward glance at the red car, and in that instant when he thought he would pass them he felt a surge of exhilaration flood up through his chest into his head, and thought, *Good old Nelly, still more than a match for a jalopy, souped or not.*

"Biff! For heaven's sake!"

He laughed, his eyes eager and happy. "We'll take 'em, honey! That race they wanted, they got it!"

The staccato snorting grew high-pitched and violent. Before he could pass, the red car was up to him, abreast of him again. He stepped harder on the accelerator, trying to push it through the floor, but his motor was whining now, complaining, and when he flicked his eyes down to the speedometer, he saw the needle wavering uncertainly at eighty-seven, where he had never seen it before. He felt the hesitations and skipping of the motor, and knew it had reached its limit. The red car skimmed ahead, snorting; went ahead easily, with the white arm hanging out the window, its fingers tapping the red door in some kind of lazy rhythm, and in seconds the red car was ahead of them on the road. The white arm lifted in an indolent wave, and then the hand, bathed in his lights, clenched itself into a fist with the thumb extended stiffly, pointed down.

He inched the car back to the right lane while the exhilaration drained out of him. It had been no race, he knew. There had been no chance to win, as in a race; there never had been a chance.

"Slow down! Biff, for heaven's sake, slow down!" Paula was leaning toward him, shouting in his ear. How long had she been shouting? he wondered, and felt a cramp in his right leg, surprised to find his foot still jamming the accelerator against the floor. His fingers were clamped around the wheel as if tightened there with steel bands. It took an actual effort to lift his foot, and they slowed down quickly—seventy, sixty, fifty, forty-five. Forty-five seemed slow, and the wind had stopped yowling at their windows.

"Don't you ever do a thing like that again!" Paula panted, glaring at him. "Never again, you hear me? Never again!"

He glanced back over his shoulder at Ruth. She was awake, sitting rigidly, her hands dug into the seat on both sides of her. Her eyes were wide, frightened.

The red car had slowed down, too, slowing more, coming closer again to them. Lazily, it drifted back almost on top of them, and they were back to thirty miles an hour. Again, gracefully, the white arm came out, waving them ahead.

"Biff!"

"Don't worry," he muttered. "The race is over." Why didn't they go away? Why didn't they just go away? And now he thought of the red car as his enemy; no longer a playful nuisance, but an enemy hounding him, forcing him to drive thirty miles an hour on this empty, straight road.

"Biff," Paula said in a few moments, "let's just stop for a little while. Why not pull off the road and stop? They'll just go away if we stop. I'm—well, I'm afraid, Biff."

"Not on your life," he snapped. "Who do they think they are? I'm not a child to be pushed around like this." He looked at her and saw her biting her lip nervously, staring hard at the red car so close ahead. "Oh, honey!" He reached over and patted her shoulder. "Sorry I snapped at you like that. But, look—as long as we keep going, it's going to be all right. They'll get bored. They'll look for somebody else to race, the fools. Just relax, honey. We'll get there a little later, that's all."

Ruth piped up from the back seat. She was fine again. "Why'n't you just beat 'em, dad?" she said. "Gee, they're going so slow, you could beat 'em. I know——"

"Ruth, please be quiet. Let daddy alone." Paula reached back and patted Ruth's knee, but not for a second did she take her eyes off the red car. The white arm was still waving them on, indolently.

A flash of anger hit him and he hooked his thumb over the horn ring and blew his horn, a long blast, and was immediately sorry he had done that. A horn on this road, like a wail in a vacuum. What good was his horn?

But the horn actually broke the spell somehow, and there were sparks from the twin exhausts, sputtering the red car into sudden life. It shot ahead swiftly, leaving the road dark and deserted ahead of them.

Wonder what those maniacs put under that hood? he thought, and said, "Could be they're tired of us slowpokes. Maybe we've seen the last of them."

"I hope so, Biff. Lord, I hope so!" Paula answered, and after a few more minutes, as the road stayed dark and deserted ahead, she settled back in her seat.

He increased his speed to forty-five, and drove tensely ahead, watching the road as if that, too, had suddenly become an enemy. There was nothing up ahead, nothing one instant, and the next instant the two taillights flashed on not two hundred feet in front of him on the road, bright and red, like a monster's eyes. The red car had been sitting on the road without lights, waiting for him. He jammed on the brake and the nose of his car dipped hard with a squeal coming from his tires, but there had been no need for him to do that, because the red car's rear wheels tore against the concrete of the road and accelerated so quickly that he could not have hit it if he had wanted to. They knew he would hit his brake just like that; just as they had known what he would do in Crockerville, and since Crockerville. That was the thing he thought of as the red car shot forward, fast, sputtering ahead, quickly losing itself in distance.

He sucked in his breath as if coming up from a fall into cold water, and then he heard the crying from the back seat. He looked back to see Ruth piled up into a ball on the floor, wailing.

"She's hurt, Biff! Stop the car!" Paula had her door open even before he had the car stopped on the shoulder of the road, and she jumped out to reach for Ruth. He got out on his side and ran around the car. Ruth was standing on the hard-packed dirt of the shoulder, her face buried in Paula's waist.

He took Ruth to the front of the car and they examined her in the light. There was nothing wrong except for a scrape on her elbows and a skinned knee, and in a moment the girl stopped crying.

Why'd you do that?" she glared at him, hiccuping. "That was a dumb thing to do, all right!"

"I won't do it again, rabbit," he said slowly. "Come on. Everything's fine now. Get in the car."

He saw Paula looking at him, her eyes enormous, frightened. She helped Ruth into the car and slid in herself.

"Biff, do you think we ought to go back to Crockerville?" Paula said, her voice pinched and dreadful. "Didn't you say something about—about having the car checked or something?"

Ruth's face twisted up at him quickly. "You promised we'd be at Aunt Mildred's tonight," she accused. "The kids'll be waiting up; you know that, dad! We got to go to Waco tonight; you said we would."

"Look, Paula," he said finally. "We're over twenty miles out of Crockerville. It really doesn't make any difference which way we go, you understand? Either they're—I mean, either we've had the last of the trouble or, if we have any more, we can stop somewhere up ahead—call in from a ranch house, you know?"

He got out, went around to the trunk and got out the long
jack handle, and then went back to his seat, placing the jack
handle on the floor of the car in the back.

Paula was near to tears. "Why not just stay here until morning?" she said, quavering, not sure of herself at all. "By then
the trouble will be gone. Biff? Biff? Why not? It's not cold."

"No!" She should know that much about him. There were
limits. That she should know after eleven years of marriage.
He felt a small flash of anger directed at her—that she should
think it was in him to sit parked on the side of the road all
night because of that red car.

He drove out on the road, peering ahead. The road was
empty, dark ahead of his lights. But as he drove he began to
think of the signs back there in Crockerville—sixty miles to the
next town. What was it now? Terrence? That was it. Terrence.
A few gasoline stations, a store or two, a motel.

Forty miles to go to Terrence, along this familiar, well-
remembered road, straight, with no turns, with nothing on
it but him and that red car, making the road an enemy for the
first time. When he thought of that—just him and that red car—
he lost his anger at Paula, and considered for an instant turning
around to rush back to Crockerville. But that would do no
good, the road was an enemy that way too; and he then considered doing as she suggested—pulling off the road to wait for
morning. . . . No!

Then there was a faint glow on the road far ahead. A car
coming, coming so fast that he knew it was the red car coming,
maybe going home, back to Crockerville at last. He gripped
the wheel hard, waiting for the red car to pass them, eager for
it to pass, and still worried about the red car coming.

But the red car was coming down his lane, on the wrong
side of the road. He felt his chest freeze and blinked his eyes,
not believing such a thing was happening, and then opened
them wide, almost in fascination as the red car kept coming
down his lane, its lights blinding, piercing, hurtling straight
at them. The breath stopped in his throat.

Paula and Ruth shrieked together, and still he was frozen, unable to breathe or move, until the lights were leaping at him, almost on him, and at last he convulsively jerked on his wheel to his left and drove his car off the road on the shoulder on the other side, into the dirt.

"Chicken!" He heard the yell from the red car clearly as it slammed by the place where his car had been, and he watched the red car careen around behind him, deftly making a screeching turn, and then it was back again, going back up the road again to Terrence.

He set the hand brake, his hands so slippery and wet he had to fumble with the brake several times before it could be done. The yell, "Chicken!" still rang in his ears and, for a moment, almost idly, he wondered what it meant, and then remembered a television program they had seen late one night—races, where two drunks got into their cars and raced at each other to see which would be the one to get out of the way. He remembered saying to Paula that such drivers deserved to be killed, and she had said she didn't believe they did such things, even drunks—a "chicken race" they had called it.

Paula had her arms around Ruth and both of them were crying, "They're going to kill us!" Paula choked, tears draining down her cheeks. "Get us out of here, Biff! Get us out of here!"

He wiped his wet hands on his trousers and stared at them, his wife and his child; all of them in his car, which was paid for; on a road which his taxes helped pay for—he stared at them until his eyes smarted.

"Chicken!" The red car would do it again. It had to. It was a ballet of some kind, a ballet in a nightmare where these things had to be played out, danced out, until the dance was ended, and the dance was not ended, that he knew.

"Chicken!" He could hear it yelling in his ears, and he could hear his wife and child sobbing, afraid and in danger of the red car, his partner in this dance—a red car, or a *Panzer* in the Vosges coming over a ridge at him, or a Messerschmitt coming in low over the trees at him near Nuremberg—the same danger, the same thing—and not to him alone, but also now to Paula and his child—and then, as it had been before with him, it was suddenly all right, and the coldness went out of his chest and went, instead, up to his head, where it could help him, as it did before.

He got out and held the door open. "Get out, Paula. Quick, now. Take Ruth and get out."

She slithered across the seat, taking Ruth with her, and stood in the dirt, still crying, looking up at him.

"Biff, please," she said, holding Ruth against her.

"Don't ask questions!" he snapped. "Take Ruth and get into that field. Don't stand there! Get going, Paula!"

He started the car slowly, back on his own side of the road, creeping ahead, alone now in the car, squinting across his lights at the sides of the road, knowing there had to be one near here, it was time for one on this road, where there were so many because the land was flat and needed drainage.

There it was, just ahead, a short concrete culvert over a drainage ditch, not a quarter of a mile from where he had left Paula and Ruth. It was like a tiny bridge, with short, heavy concrete balustrades on each side of it, the bridge just wide enough for two cars, and beneath it the ditch, dry now, crossing under the road. He drove the car over the bridge and stopped it about fifteen feet beyond, on the right side of the road, but a little over the center stripe, too, and checked to make sure his far beams were on. Then he reached into the glove compartment and got out a wrench he kept there and placed it on the accelerator, so that the motor raced a little. That was important; he had to get as much brightness to his lights as possible.

There was a flashlight in his pocket, also from the glove compartment, and then he jumped out of the car, slammed the door shut and ran down the road a little, turned back and looked at his car. His headlights blinded him so that he could not see the bridge at all. Good. He ran back to the bridge and stared up the road, remembered the jack handle, ran to the car, got it out, and stared up the road again. It had to come. The ballet was not over yet. It had to come.

And come it did. First there was a glow on the road, far ahead, and then the glow turned into two focal points of light, coming with great speed at him—on the wrong side of the road.

A vast exultation shook him, and almost too late he jumped over the balustrade and crouched in the culvert. He wanted terribly to watch the red car itself, and in his mind he did see it, very accurately, as the red car hurtled down the wrong side of the road, knowing he would turn away at the last instant, knowing that about him, as the red car knew it before—but not this time. A flashing realization—too late—that he was not going to turn away this time, a wild turn of the wheel—a balustrade sharply etched in the lights, not supposed to be there, a shriek and a wilder turn at the wheel, and then noise—a tremendous amount of noise. . . . Chicken!

The red car finally came to a stop, upright, a hundred yards into the field to the right of the road it had come racing down, whole and intact a few seconds before. It had cleared the ditch as if on wings, and had buried its nose in the field, plunging on like a wild plow making an insane furrow; at last shuddering to a stop with its front wheels crumpled and its lights still glowing, one pointed at right angles to the car and the other sending a beacon into the sky.

He had never covered a hundred yards faster in his life. The driver's door was open, sagging like a broken wing. He saw the white shirts inside, and flashed his light at them. They had their hands over their faces, and the one that was not the driver was being violently, convulsively sick, spoiling his white shirt. There was no broken glass and no blood, and he could see, from the way they were sitting, that they were not badly hurt, if at all.

A wild anger at them made him grunt like an animal, and swearing at them through this spouting well of anger, he pulled first the driver, and then the other one, out of the red car onto the field, where they sagged against the side of the car, still holding their faces in their hands. Digging his fists into each one of the

white shirts, he dragged them like bags of wheat to the headlight
that was pointed at the sky and stood them there, pulling their
hands violently away from their faces, and raised the jack handle,
ready and wanting to use it.

They were children. The faces of children stared up at him,
blinking their staring, children's eyes at him, whimpering like
children; and when they saw the jack handle, they raised their
arms over their heads, like children, and began to yammer. The
driver could not have been eighteen, and the other even younger.
He looked down at them, and much of the anger left him, but
not all.

Something had to be done to get the rest out, he knew.
Children! All the way from Crockerville—Ruth terrified and
sobbing; Paula hysterical in a field alone in the dark—children
in a red car.

The red car. He saw that the hood of it was wrenched loose,
and he yanked it open. There it was—the bright chrome of the
air scoops, the special milled head, the four-barrel carburetors—
all of it that gave the red car its special life. He began to hammer
at these things with the jack handle until there was a jagged,
broken mess under the hood, and the jack handle was bent in
his hand, and then the rest of the anger left him.

The two boys were gaping at him, and then at the red car,
and he realized that when the life went out of the red car, when
the power of the red car died, much of them died, too, and they
were left nothing, alone and powerless with their dead car in
the field.

He started to walk back to the road, but when he looked back,
he saw the boys standing where he had left them, in the glare of
the insane light. There was something indecent about the picture
he saw, so he went back, reached into the red car and snapped
off its lights.

"O.K., come on, you two!" he said, not too roughly. "I'll take
you into Terrence with us. Call the sheriff from there." And
then the three of them went back to the road, where they found
Paula and Ruth waiting by his car, waiting for him.

Readings

1. Excerpt from George Washington's "Farewell Address"

This government, the offspring of our choice uninfluenced and unawed, adopted upon full investigation and mature deliberation, completely free in its principles, in the distribution of its powers, uniting security with energy, and containing within itself a provision for its own amendment, has a just claim to your confidence and support. Respect for its authority, compliance with its laws, acquiescence in its measures, are duties enjoined by the fundamental maxims of true liberty. The basis of our political systems is the right of the people to make and to alter their constitutions of government. But the constitution which at any time exists, till changed by an explicit and authentic act of the whole people, is sacredly obligatory upon all. The very idea of the power and the right of the people to establish government, presupposed the duty of every individual to obey the established government.

2. Excerpt from Henry David Thoreau's "Civil Disobedience"

Can there not be a government in which majorities do not virtually decide right and wrong, but conscience?—in which majorities decide only those questions in which the rule of expediency is applicable? Must the citizen ever for a moment, or in the least degree, resign his conscience to the legislator? Why has every man a conscience, then? I think that we should be men first, and subjects afterward. It is not desirable to cultivate a respect for the law, so much as for the right. The only obligation which I have a right to assume is to do at any time what I think right. It is truly enough said, that a corporation has no conscience; but a corporation of conscientious men is a corporation *with* a conscience.

RICHARD VINCENT

Bad Call

Down the line came Willy and he slid hard into the catcher, and the crowd shouted and shouted. After George made the call, he swung around and walked away because he saw the genuine shock and outrage on the face of Willy Wolf, lying there in the dust. Willy really thought he was safe, George could tell. He knew Willy would come after him and he did. He screamed at George and he was mad for sure.

George could have thrown him out for some of the things he said, but he didn't because he knew Willy wasn't screaming to please the crowd or his manager or anybody else. Willy felt hurt and cheated. He pointed his reaching face toward George and said something violent, and even then George didn't throw him out. In the thirteen years Willy had played in the major leagues he had never argued with George like this, so George took it seriously and he felt sorry for Willy, but he was out at home. George had seen it and called it and that ended it forever.

He didn't blame Willy, he knew well what it meant to him. It meant money and security, fame and position, all these things, but most of all his pride as a professional competing athlete. George had never, in thirteen years, seen Willy so mad. He looked at him sadly, and, although he would never change his decision, he would have given anything else to help him. But at this point George was so sure of his decision that he never thought of the possibility that it had been wrong. Willy raised his hand as if to push and George sighed privately, deep inside himself. Now he had to throw Willy out. He couldn't remember the last time Willy had been thrown out.

He didn't do it, because Willy's manager, Al Summers, stepped between them just at the crucial moment, with that innate timing that perks infallibly inside all good managers. Al pushed Willy back into the hands of the first-base coach.

"George," he said; "George, what you doing to us?"

"I called him out," said George calmly; "that's it."

"George," said Summers, "I know you ain't going to change it, but you blew it all over the place."

"Maybe," said George, "but that's it."

Summers looked at him for a moment and he didn't seem angry, just speculative.

"George," he said finally, "you've missed a lot of them lately."

That hurt. George was quietly and greatly angry at once. Al Summers was an old friend and should never have said something like that to George.

"Al," he said, and he couldn't help it, his anger peeked out, "take it real easy, Al."

Al knew the seriousness of what he had said, George knew that, and when Al didn't back up or even look embarrassed, for the first time in many years George felt a little painful thread of indecision inside him. He had been very sure of his call.

Al knew the rules of the game, he had given George nothing but respect for years, but this time he meant what he said and he said it again.

"You missed it, George," he said; "you did. And you've missed others in this series. You're gonna cost me this ball game too. You've missed too many and it's hurting me and my ball club and I ain't gonna put up with it." He turned away from George and walked away with Willy, holding him by the arm.

Even then George thought he was right, but when he went back to brush off the plate and saw the small smile on the face of the catcher, then he knew for sure he had missed it. It wasn't that that bothered him so much, because he had missed before; not often, but once in a while he had known he was wrong. Now it was the other thing Al Summers had said that made him feel a little sick—that he had missed a lot of them lately.

The game went for fourteen innings and Al Summers' team finally lost it because of that one play. Willy Wolf came up to bat two more times before the game was over, but he didn't say anything about the call, so George knew he was taking it hard. To make everything much worse, with runners on second and third and two out in the fourteenth and the count three and two on Willy, George had to call a third strike on him that ended the game. Willy didn't argue at all. He just turned and looked at George for a moment with no expression on his face and then walked away.

A few minutes later on his sports show, Joe Cutler mentioned the call. They were sitting in a small room deep in the innards of the Stadium. Two television cameras were moving here and there on the silent rubber wheels, jockeying for angles.

He didn't mind that Joe brought it up, because he had the right to. It was the play that had turned the game around, and that made it news and important to an honest reporter like Joe.

"Willy was a mite disturbed down there," said Joe; "you might even say he was cardinal red."

"He was," said George in agreement.

"Well," said Joe, "it was a close one, George, and I'm sure you've seen others just like it."

"I have," said George; "plenty."

"Well," said Joe, "you're the dean, the top man around this league, George." He paused and when he saw George casting around in his mind for something to answer, he went smoothly on like the great interviewer he was. "And like Bill Klem you've probably never missed a call in your life." Joe laughed pleasantly.

"Well," said George, "Bill probably missed some, like me, but what he meant was that he was the umpire and when he called it, right or wrong, it stayed called."

"And it did, too," said Joe, "didn't it?"

"Always," said George.

"In all his years he didn't miss many though, did he, George?"

"I didn't see him too often," said George. "He was in the other league, but the times I saw him he didn't miss any."

"How long have you been in this league, George?" asked Joe.

"Twenty-six years," said George.

"Well then," said Joe, "you've seen most of the good ones, eh?"

"A lot of them," said George.

"If you had to do it over again," asked Joe, "would you do it?"

George started to say yes mechanically, because that was the answer, but unaccountably he hesitated, and Joe, very sensitive to his guests, looked at him sharply.

"Yes," said George, "I sure would."

When he got back to the umpires' room the three other umpires were almost ready to leave. George went to the cooler and got out a can of beer and sat down heavily on the bench in front of his locker. He started to drink, then dropped his arm and unbuckled his belt and unzipped his trousers. Then he raised the can to his lips and drank deeply with great pleasure. He lowered his head, closed his eyes and looked at himself for a moment. He was tired, too tired. His head ached and his insides were making noises. He listened to his body with the inward ear. The doctor, his family doctor, quickly and quietly visited, had said he was all right; it was just the slowing down, the blunting of the awareness and instincts of the young. Nothing to cut out, no drug to be taken, no danger of sickness or death. It was a man growing old able to do the things of before, but less quickly and less surely. He looked across at Sam Fortunato, who was almost as old as he was. Almost.

"A long one," he said to Sam.

"Too long," said Sam. He looked at George and then looked away. He stood and patted his tie into place. He took a yellow envelope from his pocket and handed it to George. "Telegram came while you was on Joe's show," he said. George took it from him. "See you," said Sam, and went out.

George watched him go. He had been about to ask Sam to share a steak with him and, maybe later, a little gin rummy in the hotel room. They had had a gin game going for almost twenty years. They didn't play every time they worked together, but almost every time.

He opened the telegram and read it. It was from the president of the league and he wanted to see George tomorrow morning. George read it again, then stuffed it into his pocket.

"George," said Hank Wilson, and he went out too.

"See you tomorrow, George," said Steve Bovik.

"Yeah," said George; then, "Steve?"

"Yeah?" Steve stopped at the door and turned.

"How about a steak?"

Steve came back into the room and he was very pleased. "Sure, George; I'd like to."

"O.K.," said George; "wait'll I shower."

"Sure," said Steve, "take your time."

Steve was a freshman in the league. He was a very good umpire now, and one day he would be close to the best. All the umpires in the major leagues were good, but there are good, better and best. George was the best, even the sports writers said so, which was almost as important as having somebody like Casey Stengel say so, and he had. George had never before asked Steve to eat with him and he saw the pleasure spread on the young man's face.

Even after the steak and the potatoes and the salad, it wouldn't go away from George. He enjoyed at intervals the deference that young Steve Bovik showed him, he answered with a measure of enthusiasm his questions about the good ones that had come and were now gone, but the other kept coming back. Willy Wolf and his unbelieving face, and the words of Al Summers, an honorable man.

Poor Willy. If it had been another player it might have been different, at least on that particular call. But Willy Wolf was a true professional. He didn't grandstand, he didn't showboat. He played the game for all it was worth and more; he didn't need to hold an umpire up to ridicule to satisfy a lack of ability. He had the ability and the joy of the game inside him, and when he was safe because of a combination of his judgment, his speed, and his great talent for the game for which he lived, he wanted to be called safe because he deserved it. Willy wouldn't dislike him even now, but he wouldn't respect him any more, and neither would Al Summers, who had virtually said as much. George had earned their respect by his own special talent and he had to keep it. He cut young Bolvik off in mid-sentence.

"Listen, Steve," he said, "I've got to see somebody; O.K.?"

Steve sat back in the booth. "Sure, George," he said.

"We'll eat again tomorrow," George said; "then maybe a little gin rummy?"

"Sure, George," said Steve and he looked happy again.

George went to the hotel on the Grand Concourse where some players had rooms and called Bucky Smith on the house phone. Bucky didn't sound surprised, but he hesitated before he said, "Sure, Georgie; come on up."

George and Bucky didn't look alike, but they were the same breed and very similar. They were in the last fifteen years of their lives—big men, heavy, and ruddy and leathery in the face. They were both overweight, but in a large strong way, and they looked more physically competent than most fat men. Their skin and muscles still had the good tone of outdoor men, which they were even during the fall and winter when they got their dogs and guns out and went hunting down South.

Bucky was alone and they sat down opposite each other. George didn't say anything at first. Bucky didn't ask anything either. The visit was unusual even though they were good friends and had played ball together years before and fished and hunted together in the fall and late winter. George held his drink in front of his big chest and glanced at Bucky.

"Looks like you got another winner, Buck," he said.

"Maybe," said Bucky; "you never can tell."

"Fifteen games," said George, "three weeks to go. Even Casey didn't do any better."

"It looks good," said Bucky cautiously; "we might make it."

"You've made it," said George.

"Well," said Bucky, "Henry's got them leg miseries biting at him again. He's playing when he should be sitting, but he's shooting for that average again."

"I missed it, didn't I, Buck?" said George.

Bucky looked at George directly, then sighed slightly like a small boy. "Yeah," he said, "you missed it all right."

"I thought so," said George, "what with what Willy and Al said."

"It hurt 'em," said Bucky; "you can't blame 'em."

"I don't," said George; "Al said something else though."

"I know," said Bucky; "he told me."

"He said I been missing a lot of them lately."

"I know," said Bucky. "He told me that too."

George sat back and looked away from Bucky. "Well?"

"I'm glad you come up, Georgie. I was gonna have to talk to you anyhow." He was standing now and he had the look, dogged and distasteful, that warned George before he heard it. "It happens that way sometimes, Georgie. It ain't anybody's fault. You got it one day and you lost it the next. I tell you truly in the years I seen you out there I don't think you missed more'n two calls. I ain't never before seen a umpire so close and so right on top of everything." He put his hand on top of his gray grizzled head as if to hold the top of it down. "Georgie, you already missed three in this series, maybe four. Last series you had with us, you missed a coupla more. I'm glad you come up, Georgie, 'cause I was gonna ask the commissioner not to use you in the World Series. I woulda told you first, Georgie, you know that, but I'm gonna ask. It ain't

only that them Milwaukees ain't like these here scufflers in this
here league. About you I just had to be sure."

"You sure, Buck?"

"Yeah, Georgie," said Bucky; "there ain't no question in my
mind. You worked almost every Series for twenty years,
Georgie, and it was right you should, but I can't have you in there
this year. You call one like you called on Willy against me,
Georgie, and I couldn't never put up with it. Them Milwaukees
ain't Washington or somebody, I gonna need all I got without
no trouble from you fellers."

"You sure you ain't already asked the commissioner?" asked
George. "I got a telegram to meet the league president tomorrow
here."

"Georgie," said Bucky, and his tough old face showed his
hurt plainly, "that ain't nothing to say to me."

"I know it," said George, "but what the hell!"

"Look, Georgie," said Bucky, "we all gotta get out sooner or
later."

"I don't want out," said George. "I want things to stay just
like they are. What am I gonna do all summer?"

"Aw, come on, Georgie," said Bucky and he sounded a little
angry. George knew why, too, and he wished he hadn't said what
he had. Bucky knew how George felt about the business; he
ought to, he felt the same way.

"Yeah," said George. "Well, it's been fun."

"Have a drink," said Bucky. "We'll play some gin and make
a night of it."

It was exactly the right thing to say, and it could cost Bucky
plenty. If a prowling writer should catch the two of them—a
manager and an umpire drinking and gambling together—Bucky
would be spending his summers with George. It was innocent,
but it wasn't to people who didn't belong or understand or who
got their own morality into it. George knew he was exposing
Bucky to much more than he should, but he would have done the
same thing for Bucky, so they drank and played until six o'clock

in the morning and George won four dollars and sixty-two cents, the first time he had ever beaten Bucky, who was a champion in gin rummy too.

George met President Wilson the next morning at eleven o'clock in the president's hotel suite.

The president was a handsome man, even dapper, beautifully dressed, including two enormous cuff links. He looked very much like a successful business executive. He was a successful business executive. Baseball was his business and he ran it like one and was paid a very high salary for doing it well and according to the wishes of the owners. He was comparatively new in the job and was trying to satisfy everybody, and it made him a nervous man at night.

He greeted George warmly, shaking his hand; then he indicated a chair and George sat down in it. There was a big desk in the room and the president stood behind it.

"How have you been, George?" asked the president, looking down at him.

"Fine, sir," said George.

That was all he said, because he had never particularly liked the man. Rather he felt ill at ease, alien, with a man like the president. He wasn't going to help him; the president wasn't somebody like Bucky or Al or Willy Wolf. He had been an important lawyer in the East before the owners hired him.

"George," said the president briskly when he saw that George had said all he was going to say, "George, I have your medical report here from the league doctor. It says you are in excellent health; exceptional in fact, for a man your age. Even your eyes are twenty-twenty, so what I have to say may sound ridiculous, but I have to say it. For the good of the game. I hate to say it, but I'm sure you'll understand. George, I'm going to have to ask for your resignation after the regular season is over." He shook his head sadly to show George where his real loyalties lay. "I've had four managerial complaints that say that you are making a lot of errors in judgment. This office also requested opinions from some of your fellow umpires, and three of them—very reluctantly, I assure you—agreed with the complaints. Now, we can do this very gracefully, George, and there will be no stigma on you. We all get older, there's no shame in that. We'll wait until the season is over, then the announcement will come from here, with regret of course and maybe even a little ceremony. You've been a credit to the game and all that, you know, sort of a——"

"I quit," said George, "right now."

"What?" The president was startled.

"I resign," said George, "right now."

"No, no," said the president, "not now. There's a way to do this and I think I am the judge of——"

"Do you think I'm missing plays, sir?"

"Well, the reports are here. I have very little choice."

"All right," said George, "I believe you. I quit."

Two lines appeared suddenly next to the president's neat nose. "You can't quit now, three weeks before the end. There's no reason for it. You can——"

"No reason?" George stood up. "I'm missing calls. I'm cheating men like Al Summers and Willy Wolf. That's too much reason. I'm not going to cheat men like that. If I can't do my job the way it should be done, I'm not working another game."

"No one said anything about cheating," said the president. "Don't get excited, George. There are only three weeks left. Bucky's boys are in. Nobody can catch them. After this series you can umpire games for Washington or Kansas City or somebody like that. If you miss some, it won't make any difference. I think you owe that to us, George."

"I don't owe you anything," said George, "I owe something to fellers like Bucky Smith and Paul Richards and Al Lopez and Al Summers; not to you."

"I understand how you feel, George, believe me," said the president, "but this has to be done right; I insist."

"Listen to me, Wilson," said George, and he was aware he

was doing something he would not like in somebody else. "Listen to me. Washington ain't gonna win any pennant, you're right. Neither is Kansas City. My missing something again don't matter in the standings. But it matters to me and it matters to Cookie Lavagetto and Harry Craft and every player on them ball clubs. They play games to win; and when you don't win many, they all count. If you figure I'd take the responsibility for taking a game away from Cookie just because I'm an old man that can't see right no more, you're wrong. I ain't gonna do that for you or anybody else. When a ump starts to miss up here he goes out right away and he don't ump no more, not one play."

The president was disturbed, but under excellent control. "That's very admirable, George, I'm sure. And I mean that. But you don't quit now, because I won't let you. I've had no umpire trouble since I've been in this job and I'm not going to have any now. We felt we owed it to you to handle it like this. We know when to be grateful and it's a shame that you don't. But this office pays your salary and you'll do what I say."

"The hell I will," said George. "I said I quit, and I quit. You don't even understand."

The president stared at George for a moment. "I don't have to understand, George," he said, "but actually I understand very well. You love the game. I love it too; don't think I don't. You wouldn't help it by quitting three weeks before the end of the season. Some snoop of a writer will comment and maybe some fans will think something's wrong. I—this office can't afford that and, what is more to the point, doesn't want to afford it. We've got to stand together here for the good of the game. I ask you as a favor to me to stay until the end of the season."

"I quit," said George. "I quit, I quit, I quit."

"I don't think you understand," said the president and his voice was strained.

"No," said George, "I don't think I do. And I ain't too sure I want to. I'm not sure this is the game that it used to be. Maybe it's better I'm getting out, because maybe it ain't good for me any more. Maybe when Bucky and Casey and Al are out of it, it won't even be a game. And I'll be glad I ain't in it and I'll sit around on my porch with Bucky and play gin and we'll remember the way it was, and even fellers with"—George fumbled a moment—"with cuff links and all"—involuntarily the president blinked down at his cuffs—"can't take that away. I quit and I do it now. I'll write you a letter."

"George," said the president, "I'm surprised at you."

"I'm surprised at myself," said George, "but I mean it."

"I know you do," said the president, "and believe it or not I'm on your side. But it is very irregular and I don't want you to do it. Very irregular."

"Not for me," said George; "it's the way I work."

He went out, leaving the door open. The president watched him go and after a moment he shook his handsome head and it could have been with reluctant respect.

George went to the stadium and picked up his equipment. It was one o'clock and the two teams were taking batting and field-ing practice. While he was in the umpires' room the three others came in together. They saw George packing his little bag.

"George," said Sam Fortunato, "what are you doing?"

"I just quit, Sam," said George, and zipped the bag shut and stood up. He put out his hand. "So long, Sam."

"George," said Sam, "what the hell. Just like that?"

"Just like that," said George, and they shook hands. He shook hands with the two other umpires. "Sorry about that gin game tonight, kid," he said to Bovik as he was leaving.

He stayed in the hotel room the whole afternoon watching the game on television. They played it with three umpires and as far as George could tell they didn't miss one, and some were close. Bucky had a fifteen-game lead, but he played it to win the whole way, as if it were the World Series. Bucky didn't know how to let up, and that's just the way it should be.

One thing happened during the game that made George glad. Willy Wolf hit one deep over the center fielder's head in the eighth inning with two men on and ran it all the way home. George saw it coming, the shortstop took the relay from the center fielder in short center field as Willy came flying around third going all the way. The ball and the man converged as if to a magnet and Willy, without slowing a bit, hooked like an eel to the left as the catcher dived onto him. Steve Bovik was standing right on top of them, his face peering down, watching the foot going over the outside of the plate and the catcher's hands slamming down on Willy.

There was not the slightest hesitation. Bovik spread his arms wide, then spun around and walked away in an unconscious imitation of George. George felt a warmth inside spread out a little.

Willy's hit won it for Al Summers, and George turned off the set and began to pack. When he finished, he called the airport and made a reservation to Dallas that evening.

About seven he went out and ate alone, and when he came back to his room Bucky Smith was sitting there in a chair.

"Georgie," said Bucky, "a little gin rummy over to my room? Give you a chance to get more of your money back."

George blinked at him. "Can't do it, Buck. Got a plane to catch pretty soon."

"Take a later one," said Bucky. "What's the difference?"

"Not much," said George, "so I might as well get this one."

"Listen," said Bucky, "come on over to my shack."

"What for?"

"I got something to show you," said Buck vaguely.

"O.K.," said George, "let's have it."

Bucky shifted his weight around a little. "Oh, Georgie," he said, "come on over."

"I won't," said George, "I don't see no sense to it."

"I got something to show you, I said," said Bucky, and he looked like an embarrassed young boy.

"I heard you," said George, "and I got to catch a plane."

"George," said Bucky, and he didn't sound vague any more, "how long do I know you?"

"I don't know," said George, "maybe thirty-five years."

"O.K.," said Bucky, "I'm asking you. Come over to my hotel."

George looked at him for a moment. "All right," he said.

They were all there. Al Summers and Willy Wolf, Sam Fortunato, Steve Bovik and Hank Wilson. The commissioner was there and Joe Cutler was there, and some of the sports writers and lots of others whose life was the game of baseball. And League President Wilson. They were all eating and talking loudly about their game. There was an inartistic clumsy banner hung on one end of the room that said, George, the Best Umpire of Them All. George was the guest of honor, but a stranger would never know it, because no one said anything he wouldn't have said if he had met George on the street. Bucky's catcher was arguing with Steve Bovik about the call on Willy Wolf, and Bovik was just laughing at him. Al Summers and Bucky began jockeying around about a player that Bucky's team owned that played for a minor-league club.

It was a great party and George played it according to the rules. He understood what they were doing, and he acted as if the party were for somebody else.

About midnight they got down to business. Joe Cutler walked under the banner and climbed up on a chair and everyone stopped talking. George sat down and looked at the floor while Joe talked.

"Georgie quit today," said Joe in his soft, mild voice. "I don't know everything that happened, but I know he didn't have to quit today. He could have finished out the season and we all know why he didn't. We're all pretty sentimental about this game of baseball. A lot of people think it's pretty silly, grown men playing a game for kids, and other grown men, intelligent men in other ways, are writing about it and taking it seriously. They say it's just a business, cold and impersonal like any other business. They might be right, it could be silly and a waste of time, and not what we think it is. But it's a great life for whatever reason, and we all love it. It can't be too silly, though, if Georgie spent over thirty years in it, playing and umpiring. Whatever business missed Georgie because he chose baseball is infinitely poorer because of his choice. We see a lot of good men come and go in this game and even some that aren't so good, because a man doesn't have to be a good, moral, honest man just because he has exceptional reflexes. So in a way it's easy to say good-by to Georgie because everything we always want to say about men in the game and about the game itself adds up to Georgie himself. He was the best and when he stopped being the best he quit right off without thinking of another way. He's not an indispensable man, because there will be other and there are other great umpires. But the way Georgie's made inside, that's pretty nearly indispensable, because both in and out of this great game Georgie —well, Georgie is on the top of the heap and you can't get farther than the top."

Joe smiled around the room. "I'm not the best man to make this speech, really. Bucky could tell more and maybe mean more; so could Sam Fortunato or Al Summers. But my business is talking and I'm doing what I can for these men to let George know what we all feel. I have never been so honored in my entire life to speak for all these fellows, Georgie, and I pray to God Almighty that I'm doing it well." Joe paused with his great instinct for the dramatic. "We'll miss you, Georgie, we'll miss you a lot, and we thought we'd throw this thing together because maybe you would then know how much we respect you and how much we love you for being what everybody in this game wishes he could be." Joe paused again. "God bless you, Georgie," he said simply, and got off the table.

Nobody applauded or made any other mistake. Nobody asked George to make a speech. They ignored him sitting there in the chair staring at the floor. After some moments Bucky's catcher began his interminable argument about the call at home, this time with Willy Wolf, who just laughed at him. Everything went on at once, loud and very comforting to George, who finally stood up looking the way George always did. He went over to Joe Cutler and held out his hand. "Talky, ain't you, Joe?" he said. He grinned at the men standing around him, then went over to Bucky, who was talking to Al Summers about that player in the minors. He shook hands with both of them.

"I'm gonna go," he said, "I'll see you around. Maybe in the fall we'll look for some birds together."

"You know it," said Bucky; "in October."

"So long, Al," said George.

"Hang in there, Georgie," said Al. "I don't know who I'll scream at now."

"You'll find somebody," said George, "like young Bovik or old Sam."

"Hell," said Al, "I never win, anyhow."

"Yeah. Well, so long."

"Take it easy, Georgie," said Bucky. "And, George?"

"Yeah?" said George.

"Don't worry, we'll take good care of the store."

"I know you will, Buck," said George; "I know you will."

GLENDON SWARTHOUT

A Glass of Blessings

Cece was so hung her tongue clave to the roof of her mouth. She groaned. This roused Sandy and Paula who were nearly as hung. She had never been so bombed as last night, the Costume Ball in Cabin Class. Wearing the bikini she had bought in Cannes, holding high the clothesline to which were pinned damp nylon pants and a bra, she had pelvised down the stairway to flash bulbs and cheers as "Miss Drip Dry of 1958" and won first prize, a bottle of champagne she had promised The Group to uncork today.

Sandy swung out of the lower berth opposite and said they had missed lunch, which was unsensational since they always did, and of course the breakfast bit had anyway gone out with the Renaissance. Cece mumbled for an herb and Sandy stuck one between her lips and lit it for her. The three of them had thought her winning so keeno that they let themselves be talked into drinking Layaways and much later be herded down to the boys' cabin. She remembered necking up a storm with Jenk, but after that she drew a complete blank. Great with her because it must have been ultrasordid.

Like vast snakes in their lairs the propeller shafts writhed and coiled and the cabin smelled like a wrestling team after some hot hammer locks. Cece absolutely abhorred squalor. Sandy was deterging a slip in the washbasin. That was the thing about Tourist Class, the squalor, the scaly people, professors and low-budget honeymooners and schoolteachers and war wives going home to show off their S. Klein wardrobes, oh, and also being stuck down with the ship's viscera. She would never forgive her folks for sending her steerage.

Sitting in the upper berth Paula hit her head on the pipe again and asked Sandy to hand her the electric razor and said there was something under the door. Cece had not been as bombed since Rome, which had been mad, mad. They had run into Carl and Jenk at the American Express and drunk lunch at Doney's and dinner at Passetto and wound up around three A.M. with a horse-cab at the Fontana di Trevi. What was under the door was their customs declarations and a notice they were to be filled out and turned in to the Purser by eight that evening as they would dock in New York at approximately seven-thirty in the morning. Paula said she didn't know how, she was anyway too flaked out, and began to shave her legs. The floodlights on the fountain were out and she and Sandy went in wading while the boys, really bombed, tried to drive the cab into the fountain, actually getting the forelegs of the horse in the water and the animal whinnying and the cabman yelling and eventually some *carabinieri* or *cherubini* or whatever they were hauling them off to the tank. So she had never seen Keat's house or the Sistine Chapel but when she came to in the hotel that afternoon she found a dime between her toes.

Her legs dangling, accompanying herself with the razor, Paula was singing *Arrivederci, Roma*, off-key. Cece forced herself to sit up and agony out of the berth. *Arrivederci*, youth. Twenty, and what had she to look forward to? An Organization Man, three kids, and varicose veins. Possibly not even that because the summer after your junior year at Loftus was the either-or point. Either you were engaged and getting married at graduation so you pooped around home all summer building a tan or you had no prospects so you sweat the folks into giving you the Grand Tour of Europe. Half-dressed, smoke from the

cigarette watering her eyes, she leaned against a wall and took
a fix on the bottle of champagne. Sandy said to bring the declarations and their purchase receipts, the boys could help them.
Scrummaging in her luggage Paula said she had no receipts. Cece
got her hair in a tail and fumbled a rubber band around it. Our
trouble, she gloomed, is that we are the all-time unco-ordinated.
Maybe because we average about one meal a day and lack
calories. We shave legs and do washings on empty stomachs and
we have no receipts. Thought for the day: when it's over, do
they give you a receipt for life? It was also like college. Concen-
trate as she might, she could recall nothing from any of her
courses except the motley types who taught them and the beginning of some poem by some metaphysical poet which had really
clicked with her: *When God at first made man, having a glass of
blessings standing by, 'Let us,' said He, 'pour on him all we can.'*
They lipsticked and found their handbags and, with Cece lugging
the champagne, went out and down the passageway. She felt so
grisly she was afraid any minute she would barf.

They opened the door into Cabin Class with the key Carl and
Jenk had made for them by twisting a piece of coat hanger and,
walking up a deck to the lobby, found the ship's photographer
had already covered a bulletin board with developed shots taken
at the Costume Ball.

"Cece, look!" Paula shrilled.

"Oh, no." Where had she raised the nerve to wear that bikini?
She had a sensation alien to her. She wondered if it could be
anything as childish as shame.

"Miss Fleshpot of 1958," Sandy said. "You going to buy one
for the folks?"

"I am not. Let's tool before I'm recognized."

"With your clothes on?"

They decided, before going to the bar, to window-shop the
ship's store, Galeries Mirabeau. The door between Cabin and
First was open and they walked across the Grand Salon to the
store, its windows crawling with gloves, scarves, perfume, men's

ties and socks. Cece saw a man's red waistcoat with gold buttons in which her father would be really slick. She went in to price it and emerged grimacing.

"*Quanto costa?*" Sandy asked.

"Thirteen thousand francs. Around thirty dollars. I know I don't have it."

"I wish I could buy more perfume," Paula sighed.

Cece pressed her nose to the Galeries window. The vest was very sharp. She could see how great her father would be wearing it, under a brown tweed jacket, say, how its red and gold and daring would contrast with the silver at his temples and, wanting it so much, swept a second time by the alien, childlike sensation, brought a sudden, oysterous lump to her throat, angering her.

"I really need another bottle of Canasta," Paula said.

"Get off my toe," Cece snapped.

Passing back into Cabin Class they went directly to the bar. Carl and Jenk were already there, beers before them, slouched at the corner table The Group had taken over on the first day out. Sandy and Paula went on while Cece paused to give the bottle of champagne to Emil, the bartender, to chill.

Going on she was stopped by the sight of the sea, which she had not taken time to look at since Southampton, blue and glittering and really oceanic, so perfect its undulance that it seemed to have been sprayed with a wave-set product from some cosmic container, so illimitable its beauty that she was absolutely clutched.

After Emil brought the girls beers they began to play bridge as they always did after missing lunch until second dinner sitting at eight, drinking and dealing and often, when they progressed from beer to liquor around five, singing school songs at the tops of their voices. One day, when an elderly couple had inadvertently usurped the corner table, The Group sat nearby making rude remarks until the couple left. From that point the other passengers avoided them as though they were leprous. Today the game soon disintegrated. The boys were hungover and needly. Jenk, who had another year at Dartmouth, threw in his cards every hand unless a slam were bid, and Carl, who had flunked out of Harvard in the spring, told Cece he had bought a print of her bikini shot and would arrange for old buddies of his to run it in the *Lampoon.*

"Help us with our declarations," Sandy said.

"List your loot, that's all," Carl said.

The girls spread out their declarations.

"I tell you about ol' Carl an' I in the canal in Amsterdam?" Jenk demanded. "It was one of those night tours with the canals all lit up. We're on this boat, see, an' this guide boring the hell out of everybody in three languages."

"How do they expect you to remember everything?" Paula complained.

"What is it, you're allowed five hundred worth of stuff duty-free?" Sandy asked.

The beer made cigarettes taste better to Cece, but it was no help psychologically.

"We're already drinking our tip money," Carl said.

"You're not," Sandy said.

"I forgot about tipping!" Paula wailed, opening her handbag and counting her money.

"You get off the boat, these jokers never see you again," Jack said. "The hell with the French. They struck oil in Algeria."

Large Animal joined them. The Group had forgotten his name. He was big and smily and went to some Oriental place like Michigan State where he was going to graduate a veterinarian and specialize in Large Animals, such as cows and horses, as opposed to Small, such as dogs and cats.

"Anyway, we're on this boat in Amsterdam, ol' Carl an' I, an' we're bombed of course or we'd never go on a damn tour. The boat comes up this water gate an' the guide hollas out to open up an' the gate guy is out to lunch. So there we sit, about eighty passengers, an' dark as hell."

"Emil, *garçon*, beers, hey!" Carl called.

Large Animal was showing the girls his completed declaration. He was good for laughs and he made a date for Paula so they tolerated him. But he was a real cube.

"What's a Bavarian bird?" Sandy asked.

He tried to explain. He had done Europe on a shoestring and the bird, a gift for his mother, which he had bought in Lucerne, not Bavaria, was his only declarable purchase.

"Animal, I didn't know you had a human mother," Carl said. "I thought you were anyway dropped in some field."

"Funny," Cece said.

"Go bring it," Paula ordered him. The beer was getting to her. "I wanna see a Bavarian bird."

"Well, ol' Carl an' I climb out on the poop deck an' shinny up the canal wall to find the gate guy. But there's nobody in the gatehouse an' we don't have the faintest how to work the machinery."

Cece was listing gifts. English doeskin gloves for her sister, five dollars. Small bottle of *Numéro Cinq* for her mother, six. Her purchases for herself came to two hundred four. Her father had given her, besides the boat ticket, a thousand to spend for the six weeks. Fourteen dollars for gifts out of a thousand.

Emil brought the beers.

"I'll never know," Sandy said, "going into my last year of school, why I bought six cashmeres."

Cece wanted the red waistcoat bitterly.

Large Animal returned with his mother's gift. It was a small metal canary perched in a large hand-painted cage. Under the tail a tiny key, when fully wound, caused the bird to sing for half an hour. A button at the base of the cage started and stilled it. He wound the key, pressed the button.

The bird tweeted.

Large Animal listened with rapture. The Group sat stunned. It was so hicky, in such bad taste, that they were speechless. Large Animal turned it off.

"Emil, *garçon*, Screwdrivers, hey!" Carl called.

"An' peanuts!" Paula called.

"So we see light across the street an' it's a bar or something so we can go in an' try to clue these jokers there's a boat can't get through the damn gate. 'Der boot iss schtuck!' we keep sayin'. Who knows any Dutch?"

Cece was counting her money. The francs and American and one traveler's cheque came to twenty-eight dollars and some cents. Her folks, driving in from Short Hills, would meet her at the pier, but even acing the dining and cabin stewards and Emil out of their tips would leave her short and, besides, she did not want to be that cruddy.

"Animal, I think it's absolutely charming and your mother will be made for it," Sandy told him, winking at the others.

Emil brought the Screwdrivers.

" 'Der boot iss schtuck!' we say but we can't get our message through to these jokers. Everybody's drinkin' this Dutch gin called Bols or something so what the hell, we have one."

"Are we playing bridge, hey?" Carl demanded.

Cece drank half her Screwdriver and had some peanuts. Jenk was anyway the bore of the world. Twenty years old and a beer belly and beer jowls and partly bald. To imagine kissing him was to barf. And what a beast.

"So we go on drinkin' Bols an' sayin' 'Der boot iss schtuck!' an' after a while we're so plowed we take off for the hotel. Could be that damn boat's still stuck in that damn canal!"

Large Animal had wandered off to the deck to look at the sea, leaving the Bavarian bird on the table.

"We heard that story the first day out," Cece said.

Paula pressed the button.

"And the second day out."

The bird tweeted.

"What's her problem?" Jenk asked injuredly.

"Paula, shut off that bird," Cece said.

"Oh, she's gone ape over a red vest in the store. For her father," Sandy explained.

"But I love it!" Cece wailed.

"Her father?" Carl tossed peanuts into his mouth. "What complex is that, hey? Oedipus or something?"

"Shut it off!" Cece commanded.

"The opposite," Sandy said, trying to remember her Psych. "Daughter for father. Electra, I think."

Cece was recounting her money. "Five to the cabin steward and ten in the dining room and maybe five for Emil."

"Who tips?" Jenk belched.

"How much is the jiving vest?" Carl asked.

Cece closed her eyes and chug-a-lugged her Screwdriver. She got spastic inside. "Sandy, my four cashmeres. I'll sell you the lot for twelve dollars."

"Cece, you know I don't have it."

"Paula, you can wear my size," Cece begged. "How about them for three apiece—they cost eighteen!"

"When you absolutely ruin the last afternoon of my summer?" Paula sniffed.

"*Voilá!*"

It was Emil bearing the champagne in a silver bucket. The Group cheered. He placed the bucket and glasses on the table beside the Bavarian bird.

"No," Cece said, swaying up. "Emil, wait. How much would that bottle be if I ordered it from you?"

"Twelf dollare. *Pourquoi?*"

"Would you buy it back from me for ten?"

"Bud no," Emil said. "*Maintenant* we nod need."

"You won't give me anything?"

"Bedder you drink."

"Then don't open it," Cece said, tossing her head. "We're not going to have it."

Emil shrugged, slipped the bottle into the ice.

The Group stared at her as though she had announced she were entering a convent or suggested they panel the world situation. She sank into her chair and put her head down on the table.

"How chintzy can you get?" Paula demanded.

"Why not have an auction in the cabin, Cece?" Sandy offered. "We'll put up signs and sell all your stuff. That should swing the vest."

"I didn't even get to see the Sistine Chapel!" Cece sobbed.

"Don't be so damn Michigan State," Carl said.

"I wanted to see where Keats died!"

Paula tweeted the bird.

"Thirty bucks, what the hell," Jenk said. "You anyway got tonight. Put on your bikini an' sell yourself. I'll pimp for you."

Cece reared, her cheeks flaming, struck the table a blow with her fist.

"Shut up all of you! That champagne is going home to my father because I've cheaped out on him! None of us saw Europe —we went on a bombing raid! We're selfish and unco-ordinated and I hate us, hate us, hate us!"

Her eyes awash she flung her head down on her arms again. She could hear them sweeping up cards and money and declarations.

Carl punctuated the bit: "Miss Drip of 1938."

Suddenly Cece understood they would leave her. She panicked completely. She would be the all-time isolate. Word of how gung-ho and preachy and childish she had been would circulate and there would be no Group for her anywhere. She stood. She made them wait until she unfoiled and uncorked the champagne. Against tears of terror she played out the scene by serving them herself. She cried that when this bottle was killed she would buy more. She laughed that her father was anyway past the red vest phase. So terrific was she, so her real self again, that she won: they stayed, and by second sitting they were singing and absolutely stoned.

A. E. COPPARD

Dusky Ruth

At the close of an April day, chilly and wet, the traveller came to a country town. In the Cotswolds, though the towns are small and sweet and the inns snug, the general habit of the land is bleak and bare. He had newly come upon upland roads so void of human affairs, so lonely, that they might have been made for some forgotten uses by departed men, and left to the unwitting passage of such strangers as himself. Even the unending walls, built of old rough laminated rock that detailed the far-spreading fields, had grown very old again in their courses; there were dabs of darkness, buttons of moss, and fossils on every stone. He had passed a few neighbourhoods, sometimes at the crook of a stream, or at the cross of debouching roads, where old habitations, their gangrenated thatch riddled with bird-holes, had not been so much erected as just spattered about the places. Beyond these signs an odd lark or blackbird, the ruckle of partridges, or the nifty gallop of a hare, had been the only mitigation of the living loneliness that was almost as profound by day as by night. But the traveller had a care for such times and places. There are men who love to gaze with the mind at things that can never be seen, feel at least the throb of a beauty that will never be known, and hear over immense bleak reaches the echo of that which is no celestial music, but only their own hearts' vain cries; and though his garments clung to him like clay it was with deliberate questing step that the traveller trod the single street of the town, and at last entered the inn, shuffling his shoes in the doorway for a moment and striking the raindrops from his hat. Then he turned into a small smoking-room. Leather-lined benches, much worn, were fixed to the wall under the window and in other odd corners and nooks behind mahogany tables. One wall was furnished with all the congenial gear of a bar, but without any intervening counter. Opposite a bright fire was burning, and a neatly-dressed young woman sat before it in a Windsor chair, staring at the flames. There was no other inmate of the room, and as he entered, the girl rose up and greeted him. He found that he could be accommodated for the night, and in a few moments his hat and scarf were removed and placed inside the fender, his wet overcoat was taken to the kitchen, the landlord, an old fellow, was lending him a roomy pair of slippers, and a maid was setting supper in an adjoining room.

He sat while this was doing and talked to the barmaid. She had a beautiful, but rather mournful, face as it was lit by the fire-light, and when her glance was turned away from it her eyes had a piercing brightness. Friendly and well-spoken as she was, the melancholy in her aspect was noticeable—perhaps it was the dim room, or the wet day or the long hours ministering a multitude of cocktails to thirsty gallantry.

When he went to his supper he found cheering food and drink, with pleasant garniture of silver and mahogany. There were no other visitors, he was to be alone; blinds were drawn, lamps lit, and the fire at his back was comforting. So he sat long about his meal until a white-faced maid came to clear the table, discoursing to him of country things as she busied about the room. It was a long narrow room, with a sideboard and the door at one end and the fireplace at the other. A bookshelf, almost devoid of books, contained a number of plates; the long wall that faced the windows was almost destitute of pictures, but there were hung upon it, for some inscrutable but doubtless sufficient reason, many dish-covers, solidly shaped, of the kind held in such mysterious regard and known as "willow pattern"; one was even hung upon the face of a map. Two musty prints were mixed with them, presentments of horses having a stilted, extravagant physique and bestridden by images of inhuman and incommunicable dignity, clothed in whiskers, coloured jackets and tight white breeches.

He took down the books from the shelf, but his interest was speedily exhausted, and the almanacs, the county directory, and various guidebooks were exchanged for the *Cotswold Chronicle*. With this, having drawn the deep chair to the hearth, he whiled away the time. The newspaper amused him with its advertisements of stock shows, farm auctions, travelling quacks and conjurers, and there was a lengthy account of the execution of a local felon, one Timothy Bridger, who had murdered an infant in some shameful circumstances. This dazzling crescendo proved rather trying to the traveller; he threw down the paper.

The town was all quiet as the hills, and he could hear no sounds in the house. He got up and went across the hall to the smoke-room. The door was shut, but there was light within, and he entered. The girl sat there much as he had seen her on his arrival, still alone, with feet on fender. He shut the door behind him, sat down, and crossing his legs, puffed at his pipe, admired the snug little room and the pretty figure of the girl, which he could do without embarrassment as her meditative head, slightly bowed, was turned away from him. He could see something of her, too, in the mirror at the bar, which repeated also the agreeable contours of bottles of coloured wines and rich liqueurs—so entrancing in form and aspect that they seemed destined to charming histories, even in disuse—and those of families outline containing mere spirits or small beer, for which are reserved the harsher destinies of base oils, horse medicines, disinfectants, and cold tea. There were coloured glasses for bitter wines, white glasses for sweet, a tiny leaden sink beneath them, and the four black handles of the beer engine.

The girl wore a light blouse of silk, a short skirt of black velvet, and a pair of very thin silk stockings that showed the flesh of instep and shin so plainly that he could see they were reddened by the warmth of the fire. She had on a pair of dainty cloth shoes with high heels, but what was wonderful about her was the heap of rich black hair piled at the back of her head and shadowing the dusky neck. He sat puffing his pipe and letting the loud tick of the clock fill the quiet room. She did not stir and he could move no muscle. It was as if he had been willed to come there and wait silently. That, he felt now, had been his desire all the evening; and here, in her presence, he was more strangely stirred than by any event he could remember.

In youth he had viewed women as futile pitiable things that grew long hair, wore stays and garters, and prayed incomprehensible prayers. Viewing them in the stalls of the theatre from his vantage-point in the gallery, he always disliked the articulation of their naked shoulders. But still, there was a god in the sky, a god with flowing hair and exquisite eyes, whose one stride with an ardour grandly rendered took him across the whole round hemisphere to which his buoyant limbs were bound like spokes to the eternal rim and axle, his bright hair burning in the pity of the sunsets and tossing in the anger of the dawns.

Master traveller had indeed come into this room to be with this woman: she as surely desired him, and for all its accidental occasion it was as if he, walking the ways of the world, had suddenly come upon . . . what so imaginable with all permitted reverence as, well, just a shrine; and he, admirably humble, bowed the instant head.

Were there no other people within? The clock indicated a few minutes to nine. He sat on, still as stone, and the woman might have been of wax for all the movement or sound she made. There was allurement in the air between them; he had forborne his smoking, the pipe grew cold between his teeth. He waited for a look from her, a movement to break the trance of silence. No footfall in street or house, no voice in the inn, but the clock beating away as if pronouncing a doom. Suddenly it rasped out nine large notes, a bell in the town repeated them dolefully, and a cuckoo no further than the kitchen mocked them with three times three. After that came the weak steps of the old landlord along the hall, the slam of doors, the clatter of lock and bolt, and then the silence returning unendurably upon them.

He arose and stood behind her; he touched the black hair. She made no movement or sign. He pulled out two or three combs, and dropping them into her lap let the whole mass tumble about his hands. It had a curious harsh touch in the unravelling, but was so full and shining; black as a rook's wings it was. He slid his palms through it. His fingers searched it and fought with its fine strangeness; into his mind there travelled a serious thought, stilling his wayward fancy—this was no wayward fancy, but a rite accomplishing itself! *(Run, run, silly man, y'are lost!)* But having got so far he burnt his boats, leaned over, and drew her face back to him. And at that, seizing his wrists, she gave him back ardour for ardour, pressing his hands to her bosom, while the kiss was sealed and sealed again. Then she sprang up and picking his hat and scarf from the fender said:

"I have been drying them for you, but the hat has shrunk a bit, I'm sure—I tried it on."

He took them from her, and put them behind him; he leaned lightly back upon the table, holding it with both his hands behind him; he could not speak.

"Aren't you going to thank me for drying them?" she asked, picking her combs from the rug and repinning her hair.

"I wonder why we did that?" he asked shamedly.

"It is what I'm thinking too," she said.

"You were so beautiful about . . . about it, you know."

She made no rejoinder, but continued to bind her hair, looking brightly at him under her brows. When she had finished she went close to him.

"Will that do?"

"I'll take it down again."

"No, no, the old man or the old woman will be coming in."

"What of that?" he said, taking her into his arms. "Tell me your mine."

She shook her head, but she returned his kisses and stroked his hair and shoulders with beautifully melting gestures.

"What is your name, I want to call you by your name?" he said. "I can't keep calling you Lovely Woman, Lovely Woman."

Again she shook her head and was dumb.

"I'll call you Ruth then, Dusky Ruth, Ruth of the black, beautiful hair."

"That is a nice-sounding name—I knew a deaf and dumb girl named Ruth; she went to Nottingham and married an organ-grinder—but I should like it for my name."

"Then I give it to you."

"Mine is so ugly."

"What is it?"

Again the shaken head and the burning caress.

"Then you shall be Ruth; will you keep that name?"

"Yes, if you give me the name I will keep it for you."

Time had indeed taken them by the forelock, and they looked upon a ruddled world.

"I stake my one talent," he said jestingly, "and behold it returns me fortyfold; I feel like the boy who catches three mice with one piece of cheese."

At ten o'clock the girl said:

"I must go and see how *they* are getting on," and she went to the door.

"Are we keeping them up?"

She nodded.

"Are you tired?"

"No, I am not tired."

She looked at him doubtfully.

"We ought not to stay in here; go into the coffee-room and I'll come there in a few minutes."

"Right," he whispered gaily, "we'll sit up all night."

She stood at the door for him to pass out, and he crossed the hall to the other room. It was in darkness except for the flash of the fire. Standing at the hearth he lit a match for the lamp, but paused at the globe; then he extinguished the match.

"No, it's better to sit in the firelight."

He heard voices at the other end of the house that seemed to have a chiding note in them.

"Lord," he thought, "she is getting into a row?"

Then her steps came echoing over the stone floors of the hall; she opened the door and stood there with a lighted candle in her hand; he stood at the other end of the room, smiling.

"Good night," she said.

"Oh no, no! come along," he protested, but not moving from the hearth.

"Got to go to bed," she answered.

"Are they angry with you?"

"No."

"Well, then, come over here and sit down."

"Got to go to bed," she said again, but she had meanwhile put her candlestick upon the little sideboard and was trimming the wick with a burnt match.

"Oh, come along, just half an hour," he protested. She did not answer but went on prodding the wick of the candle.

"Ten minutes, then," he said, still not going towards her.

"Five minutes," he begged.

She shook her head, and picking up the candlestick turned to the door. He did not move, he just called her name: "Ruth!"

She came back then, put down the candlestick and tiptoed across the room until he met her. The bliss of the embrace was so poignant that he was almost glad when she stood up again and said with affected steadiness, though he heard the tremor in her voice:

"I must get you your candle."

She brought one from the hall, set it on the table in front of him, and struck the match.

"What is my number?" he asked.

"Number six room," she answered, prodding the wick

vaguely with her match, while a slip of white wax dropped over the shoulder of the new candle. "Number six . . . next to mine."

The match burnt out; she said abruptly "Good night," took up her own candle and left him there.

In a few moments he ascended the stairs and went into his room. He fastened the door, removed his coat, collar, and slippers, but the rack of passion had seized him and he moved about with no inclination to sleep. He sat down, but there was no medium of distraction. He tried to read the newspaper which he had carried up with him, and without realizing a single phrase, he forced himself to read again the whole account of the execution of the miscreant Bridger. When he had finished this he carefully folded the paper and stood up, listening. He went to the parting wall and tapped thereon with his finger-tips. He waited half a minute, one minute, two minutes; there was no answering sign. He tapped again, more loudly, with his knuckles, but there was no response, and he tapped many times. He opened his door as noiselessly as possible; along the dark passage there were slips of light under the other doors, the one next his own, and the one beyond that. He stood in the corridor listening to the rumble of old voices in the farther room, the old man and his wife going to their rest. Holding his breath fearfully, he stepped to *her* door and tapped gently upon it. There was no answer, but he could somehow divine her awareness of him; he tapped again; she moved to the door and whispered, "No, no, go away." He turned the handle, the door was locked.

"Let me in," he pleaded. He knew she was standing there an inch or two beyond him.

"Hush," she called softly. "Go away, the old woman has ears like a fox."

He stood silent for a moment.

"Unlock it," he urged; but he got no further reply, and feeling foolish and baffled he moved back to his own room, cast his clothes from him, doused the candle and crept into the bed with soul as wild as a storm-swept forest, his heart beating a vagrant summons. The room filled with strange heat, there was no composure for mind or limb, nothing but flaming visions and furious embraces.

"Morality . . . what is it but agreement with your own soul?"

So he lay for two hours—the clocks chimed twelve—listening with foolish persistency for *her* step along the corridor, fancying every light sound—and the night was full of them—was her hand upon the door.

Suddenly—and then it seemed as if his very heart would abash the house with its thunder—he could hear distinctly some one knocking on the wall. He got quickly from his bed and stood at the door, listening. Again the knocking was heard, and having half clothed himself he crept into the passage, which was now in utter darkness, trailing his hand along the wall until he felt her door; it was standing open. He entered her room and closed the door behind him. There was not the faintest gleam of light, he could see nothing. He whispered "Ruth!" and she was standing there. She touched him, but not speaking. He put out his hands, and they met round her neck; her hair was flowing in its great wave about her; he put his lips to her face and found that her eyes were streaming with tears, salt and strange and disturbing. In the close darkness he put his arms about her with no thought but to comfort her; one hand had plunged through the long harsh tresses and the other across her hips before he realized that she was ungowned; then he was aware of the softness of her breasts and the cold naked sleekness of her shoulders. But she was crying there, crying silently with great tears, her strange sorrow stifling his desire.

"Ruth, Ruth, my beautiful dear!" he murmured soothingly. He felt for the bed with one hand, and turning back the quilt and sheets he laid her in as easily as a mother does her child, replaced the bedding, and, in his clothes, he lay stretched beside her comforting her. They lay so, innocent as children, for an hour, when she seemed to have gone to sleep. He rose then and went silently to his room, full of weariness.

In the morning he breakfasted without seeing her, but as he had business in the world that gave him just an hour longer at the inn before he left it for good and all, he went into the smoke-room and found her. She greeted him with curious gaze, but merrily enough, for there were other men there now, farmers, a butcher, a registrar, an old, old man. The hour passed, but not these men, and at length he donned his coat, took up his stick, and said good-bye. Her shining glances followed him to the door, and from the window as far as they could view him.

DONALD BARTHELME

A Shower of Gold

Because he needed the money Peterson answered an ad that said
"We'll pay you to be on TV if your opinions are strong enough
or your personal experiences have a flavor of the unusual." He
called the number and was told to come to Room 1551 in the
Graybar Building on Lexington. This he did and after spending
twenty minutes with a Miss Arbor who asked him if he had ever
been in analysis was okayed for a program called *Who Am I?*
"What do you have strong opinions about?" Miss Arbor asked.
"Art," Peterson said, "life, money." "For instance?" "I believe,"
Peterson said, "that the learning ability of mice can be lowered
or increased by regulating the amount of serotonin in the brain.
I believe that schizophrenics have a high incidence of unusual
fingerprints, including lines that make almost complete circles. I
believe that the dreamer watches his dream in sleep, by moving
his eyes." *"That's very interesting!"* Miss Arbor cried. "It's all
in the *World Almanac,*" Peterson replied.

"I see you're a sculptor," Miss Arbor said, "that's wonderful." "What is the nature of the program?" Peterson asked. "I've
never seen it." "Let me answer your question with another question," Miss Arbor said. "Mr. Peterson, are you absurd?" Her
enormous lips were smeared with a glowing white cream. "I beg
your pardon?" "I mean," Miss Arbor said earnestly, "do you en-

counter your own existence as gratuitous? Do you feel *de trop?* Is there nausea?" "I have an enlarged liver," Peterson offered. "That's *excellent!*" Miss Arbor exclaimed. "That's a *very* good beginning! *Who Am I?* tries, Mr. Peterson, to discover what people *really are.* People today, we feel, are hidden away inside themselves, alienated, desperate, living in anguish, despair and bad faith. Why have we been thrown here, and abandoned? That's the question we try to answer, Mr. Peterson. Man stands alone in a featureless, anonymous landscape, in fear and trembling and sickness unto death. God is dead. Nothingness everywhere. Dread. Estrangement. Finitude. *Who Am I?* approaches these problems in a root radical way." "On television?" "We're interested in basics, Mr. Peterson. We don't play around." "I see," Peterson said, wondering about the amount of the fee. "What I want to know now, Mr. Peterson, is this: are you *interested* in absurdity?" "Miss Arbor," he said, "to tell you the truth, I don't know. I'm not sure I believe in it." "Oh, Mr. Peterson!" Miss Arbor said, shocked. "Don't *say* that! You'll be . . ." "Punished?" Peterson suggested. "*You* may not be interested in absurdity," she said firmly, "but absurdity is interested in *you.*" "I have a lot of problems, if that helps," Peterson said. "Existence is problematic for you," Miss Arbor said, relieved. "The fee is two hundred dollars."

"I'm going to be on television," Peterson said to his dealer. "A terrible shame," Jean-Claude responded. "Is it unavoidable?" "It's unavoidable," Peterson said, "if I want to eat." "How much?" Jean-Claude asked and Peterson said: "Two hundred." He looked around the gallery to see if any of his works were on display. "A ridiculous compensation considering the infamy. Are you using your own name?" "You haven't by any chance . . ." "No one is buying," Jean-Claude said. "Undoubtedly it is the weather. People are thinking in terms of—what do you call those things?—Chris-Crafts. To boat with. You would not consider again what I spoke to you about before?" "No," Peterson said, "I wouldn't consider it." "Two little ones would move much, much faster than a single huge big one," Jean-Claude said, looking away. "To saw it across the middle would be a very simple matter." "It's supposed to be a work of art," Peterson said, as calmly as possible. "You don't go around sawing works of art across the middle, remember?" "That place where it saws," Jean-Claude said, "is not very difficult. I can put my two hands around it." He made a circle with his two hands to demonstrate. "Invariably when I look at that piece I see two pieces. Are you absolutely sure you didn't conceive it wrongly in the first instance?" "Absolutely," Peterson said. Not a single piece of his was on view, and his liver expanded in rage and hatred. "You have a very romantic impulse," Jean-Claude said. "I admire, dimly, the posture. You read too much in the history of art. It estranges you from those possibilities for authentic selfhood that inhere in the present century." "I know," Peterson said, "could you let me have twenty until the first?"

Peterson sat in his loft on lower Broadway drinking Rheingold and thinking about the President. He had always felt close to the President but felt now that he had, in agreeing to appear on the television program, done something slightly disgraceful, of which the President would not approve. But I needed the money, he told himself, the telephone is turned off and the kitten is crying for milk. And I'm running out of beer. The President feels that the arts should be encouraged, Peterson reflected, surely he doesn't want me to go without beer? He wondered if what he was feeling was simple guilt at having sold himself to television or something more elegant: nausea? His liver groaned within him and he considered a situation in which his new relationship with the President was announced. He was working in the loft. The piece in hand was to be called *Season's Greetings* and combined three auto radiators, one from a Chevrolet Tudor, one from a Ford pickup, one from a 1932 Essex, with part of a former telephone switchboard and other items. The arrangement seemed right and he began welding. After a time the mass was freestanding. A couple of hours had passed. He put down the torch, lifted off the mask. He walked over to the refrigerator and found a sandwich left by a friendly junk dealer. It was a sandwich made hastily and without inspiration: a thin slice of ham between two pieces of bread. He ate it gratefully nevertheless. He stood looking at the work, moving from time to time so as to view it from a new angle. Then the door to the loft burst open and the President ran in, trailing a sixteen-pound sledge. His first blow cracked the principal weld in *Season's Greetings*, the two halves parting like lovers, clinging for a moment and then rushing off in opposite directions. Twelve Secret Service men held Peterson in a paralyzing combination of secret grips. He's looking good, Peterson thought, very good, healthy, mature, fit, trustworthy. I like his suit. The President's second and third blows smashed the Essex radiator and the Chevrolet radiator. Then he attacked the welding torch, the plaster sketches on the workbench, the Rodin cast and the Giacometti stickman Peterson had bought in Paris. *"But Mr. President!"* Peterson shouted. *"I thought we were friends!"* A Secret Service man bit him in the back of the neck. Then the President lifted the sledge high in the air, turned toward Peterson, and said: "Your liver is diseased? That's a good sign. You're making progress. You're thinking."

"I happen to think that guy in the White House is doing a pretty darn good job." Peterson's barber, a man named Kitchen who was also a lay analyst and the author of four books titled *The Decision To Be*, was the only person in the world to whom he had confided his former sense of community with the President. "As far as his relationship with you personally goes," the barber continued, "it's essentially a kind of I-Thou relationship, if you know what I mean. You got to handle it with full awareness of the implications. In the end one experiences only oneself, Nietzsche said. When you're angry with the President, what you experience is self-as-angry-with-the-President. When things are okay between you and him, what you experience is self-as-swinging-with-the-President. Well and good. *But,*" Kitchen said, lathering up, "you want the relationship to be such that what you experience is the-President-as-swinging-with-you. You want *his* reality, get it? So that you can break out of the hell of solipsism. How about a little more off the sides?" "Everybody knows the language but me," Peterson said irritably. "Look," Kitchen said, "when you talk about me to somebody else, you say 'my barber,' don't you? Sure you do. In the same way, I look at you as being 'my customer,' get it? But you don't regard yourself as being 'my' customer and I don't regard myself as 'your' barber. Oh, it's hell all right." The razor moved like a switchblade across the back of Peterson's neck. "Like Pascal said: 'The natural misfortune of our mortal and feeble condition is so wretched that when we consider it closely, nothing can console us.' " The razor rocketed around an ear. "Listen," Peterson said, "what do you think of this television program called *Who Am I?* Ever seen it?" "Frankly," the barber said, "it smells of the library. But they do a job on those people, I'll tell you that." "What do you mean?" Peterson said excitedly. "What kind of a job?" The cloth was whisked away and shaken with a sharp popping sound. "It's too horrible even to talk about," Kitchen said. "But it's what they deserve, those crumbs." "Which crumbs?" Peterson asked.

That night a tall foreign-looking man with a switchblade big as a butcherknife open in his hand walked into the loft without knocking and said "Good evening, Mr. Peterson, I am the cat-piano player, is there anything you'd particularly like to hear?" "Cat-piano?" Peterson said, gasping, shrinking from the knife. "What are you talking about? What do you want?" A biography of Nolde slid from his lap to the floor. "The cat-piano," said the visitor, "is an instrument of the devil, a diabolical instrument. You needn't sweat quite so much," he added, sounding aggrieved. Peterson tried to be brave. "I don't understand," he said. "Let me explain," the tall foreign-looking man said graciously. "The keyboard consists of eight cats—the octave—encased in the body of the instrument in such a way that only their heads and fore-paws protrude. The player presses upon the appropriate paws, and the appropriate cats respond—with a kind of shriek. There is also provision made for pulling their tails. A tail-puller, or perhaps I should say tail *player*" (he smiled a disingenuous smile) "is stationed at the rear of the instrument, where the tails are. At the correct moment the tail-puller pulls the correct tail. The tail-note is of course quite different from the paw-note and produces sounds in the upper registers. Have you ever seen such an instrument, Mr. Peterson?" "No, and I don't believe it exists," Peterson said heroically. "There is an excellent early seventeenth-century engraving by Franz van der Wyngaert, Mr. Peterson, in which a cat-piano appears. Played, as it happens, by a man with a wooden leg. You will observe my own leg." The cat-piano player hoisted his trousers and a leglike contraption of wood, metal and plastic appeared. "And now, would you like to make a request? 'The Martyrdom of St. Sebastian'? The 'Romeo and Juliet' overture? 'Holiday for Strings?' " "But why—" Peterson began. "The kitten is crying for milk, Mr. Peterson. And whenever a kitten cries, the cat-piano plays." "But it's not my kitten," Peterson said reasonably. "It's just a kitten that wished itself on me. I've been trying to give it away. I'm not sure it's still around. I haven't seen it since the day before yesterday." The kitten appeared, looked at Peterson reproachfully, and then rubbed itself against the cat-piano player's mechanical leg. "Wait a minute!" Peterson exclaimed. "This thing is rigged! That cat hasn't been here in two days. What do you want from me? What am I supposed to do?" "Choices, Mr. Peterson, choices. You *chose* that kitten as a way of encountering that which you are not, that is to say, kitten. An effort on the part of the *pour-soi* to—" "But it chose me!" Peterson cried, "the door was open and the first thing I knew it was lying in my bed, under the Army blanket. I didn't have anything to do with it!" The cat-piano player repeated his disingenuous smile. "Yes, Mr. Peterson, I know, I know. Things are done to you, it is all a gigantic conspiracy. I've heard the story a hundred times. But the kitten is here, is it not? The kitten is weeping, is it not?" Peterson looked at the kitten, which was crying huge tigerish tears into its empty dish. "*Listen* Mr. Peterson," the cat-piano player said, "*listen!*" The blade of his immense knife jumped back into the handle with a thwack! and the hideous music began.

The day after the hideous music began the three girls from California arrived. Peterson opened his door, hesitantly, in response to an insistent ringing, and found himself being stared at by three girls in blue jeans and heavy sweaters, carrying suitcases. "I'm Sherry," the first girl said, "and this is Ann and this is Louise. We're from California and we need a place to stay." They were homely and extremely purposeful. "I'm sorry," Peterson said, "I can't—" "We sleep anywhere," Sherry said, looking past him into the vastness of his loft, "on the floor if we have to. We've done it before." Ann and Louise stood on their toes to get a good look. "What's that funny music?" Sherry asked, "it sounds pretty far-out. We really won't be any trouble at all and it'll just be a little while until we make a connection." "Yes," Peterson said, "but why me?" "You're an artist," Sherry said sternly, "we saw the A.I.R. sign downstairs." Peterson cursed the fire laws which made posting of the signs obligatory. "Listen," he said, "I can't even feed the cat. I can't even keep myself in beer. This is not the place. You won't be happy here. My work isn't authentic. I'm a minor artist." "The natural misfortune of our mortal and feeble condition is so wretched that when we consider it closely, nothing can console us," Sherry said. "That's Pascal." "I know," Peterson said, weakly. "Where is the john?" Louise asked. Ann marched into the kitchen and began to prepare, from supplies removed from her rucksack, something called *veal engagé.* "Kiss me," Sherry said, "I need love." Peterson flew to his friendly neighborhood bar, ordered a double brandy, and wedged himself into a telephone booth. "Miss Arbor? This is Hank Peterson. Listen, Miss Arbor, I can't do it. No, I mean really. I'm being punished horribly for even thinking about it. No, I mean it. You can't imagine what's going on around here. Please, get somebody else? I'd regard it as a great personal favor. Miss Arbor? Please?"

The other contestants were a young man in white pajamas named Arthur Pick, a karate expert, and an airline pilot in full uniform, Wallace E. Rice. "Just be natural," Miss Arbor said, "and of course be frank. We score on the basis of the validity of your answers, and of course that's measured by the polygraph." "What's this about a polygraph?" the airline pilot said. "The polygraph measures the validity of your answers," Miss Arbor said, her lips glowing whitely. "How else are we going to know if you're . . ." "Lying?" Wallace E. Rice supplied. The contestants were connected to the machine and the machine to a large illuminated tote board hanging over their heads. The master of ceremonies, Peterson noted without pleasure, resembled the President and did not look at all friendly.

The program began with Arthur Pick. Arthur Pick got up in his white pajamas and gave a karate demonstration in which he broke three half-inch pine boards with a single kick of his naked left foot. Then he told how he had disarmed a bandit, late at night at the A&P where he was an assistant manager, with a maneuver called a "rip-choong" which he demonstrated on the announcer. "How about that?" the announcer caroled. "Isn't that something? Audience?" The audience responded enthusiastically and Arthur Pick stood modestly with his hands behind his back. "Now," the announcer said, "let's play *Who Am I?* And here's your host, *Bill Lemmon!*" No, he doesn't look like the President, Peterson decided. "Arthur," Bill Lemmon said, "for twenty dollars—do you love your mother?" "Yes," Arthur Pick said. "Yes, of course." A bell rang, the tote board flashed, and the audience screamed. "He's lying!" the announcer shouted, "lying! lying! lying!" "Arthur," Bill Lemmon said, looking at his index cards, "the polygraph shows that the validity of your answer is . . . questionable. Would you like to try it again? Take another crack at it?" "You're crazy," Arthur Pick said. "Of course I love my mother." He was fishing around inside his pajamas for a handkerchief. "Is your mother watching the show tonight, Arthur?" "Yes, Bill, she is." "How long have you been studying karate?" "Two years, Bill." "And who paid for the lessons?" Arthur Pick hesitated. Then he said: "My mother, Bill." "They were pretty expensive, weren't they, Arthur?" "Yes, Bill, they were." "How expensive?" "Five dollars an hour." "Your mother doesn't make very much money, does she, Arthur?" "No, Bill, she doesn't." "Arthur, what does your mother do for a living?" "She's a garment worker, Bill. In the garment district." "And how long has she worked down there?" "All her life, I guess. Since my old man died." "And she doesn't make very much money, you said." "No. But she *wanted* to pay for the lessons. She *insisted* on it." Bill Lemmon said: "She wanted a son who could break boards with his feet?" Peterson's liver leaped and the tote board spelled out, in huge, glowing white letters, the words BAD FAITH. The airline pilot, Wallace E. Rice, was led to reveal that he had been caught, on a flight from Omaha to Miami, with a stewardess sitting on his lap and wearing his captain's cap, that the flight engineer had taken a Polaroid picture, and that he had been given involuntary retirement after nineteen years of faithful service. "It was perfectly safe," Wallace E. Rice said, "you don't understand, the automatic pilot can fly that plane better than I can." He further confessed to a lifelong and intolerable itch after stewardesses which had much to do, he said, with the way their jackets fell just on top of their hips, and his own jacket with the three gold stripes on the sleeve darkened with sweat until it was black.

I was wrong, Peterson thought, the world is absurd. The absurdity is punishing me for not believing in it. I affirm the absurdity. On the other hand, absurdity is itself absurd. Before the emcee could ask the first question, Peterson began to talk. "Yesterday," Peterson said to the television audience, "in the typewriter in front of the Olivetti showroom on Fifth Avenue, I found a recipe for Ten Ingredient Soup that included a stone from a toad's head. And while I stood there marveling a nice old lady pasted on the elbow of my best Haspel suit a little blue sticker reading THIS INDIVIDUAL IS A PART OF THE COMMUNIST CONSPIRACY FOR GLOBAL DOMINATION OF THE ENTIRE GLOBE. Coming home I passed a sign that said in ten-foot letters COWARD

SHOES and heard a man singing "Golden Earrings" in a horrible voice, and last night I dreamed there was a shoot-out at our house on Meat Street and my mother shoved me in a closet to get me out of the line of fire." The emcee waved at the floor manager to turn Peterson off, but Peterson kept talking. "In this kind of a world," Peterson said, "absurd if you will, possibilities nevertheless proliferate and escalate all around us and there are opportunities for beginning again. I am a minor artist and my dealer won't even display my work if he can help it but minor is as minor does and lightning may strike even yet. Don't be reconciled. Turn off your television sets," Peterson said, "cash in your life insurance, indulge in a mindless optimism. Visit girls at dusk. Play the guitar. How can you be alienated without first having been connected? Think back and remember how it was." A man on the floor in front of Peterson was waving a piece of cardboard on which something threatening was written but Peterson ignored him and concentrated on the camera with the little red light. The little red light jumped from camera to camera in an attempt to throw him off balance but Peterson was too smart for it and followed wherever it went. "My mother was a royal virgin," Peterson said, "and my father a shower of gold. My childhood was pastoral and energetic and rich in experiences which developed my character. As a young man I was noble in reason, infinite in faculty, in form express and admirable, and in apprehension . . ." Peterson went on and on and although he was, in a sense, lying, in a sense he was not.

SARAH ORNE JEWETT

A White Heron

The woods were already filled with shadows one June evening, just before eight o'clock, though a bright sunset still glimmered faintly among the trunks of the trees. A little girl was driving home her cow, a plodding, dilatory, provoking creature in her behavior, but a valued companion for all that. They were going away from the western light, and striking deep into the dark woods, but their feet were familiar with the path, and it was no matter whether their eyes could see it or not.

There was hardly a night the summer through when the old cow could be found waiting at the pasture bars; on the contrary, it was her greatest pleasure to hide herself away among the high huckleberry bushes, and though she wore a loud bell she had made the discovery that if one stood perfectly still it would not ring. So Sylvia had to hunt for her until she found her, and call Co'! Co'! with never an answering Moo, until her childish patience was quite spent. If the creature had not given good milk and plenty of it, the case would have seemed very different to her owners. Besides, Sylvia had all the time there was, and very little use to make of it. Sometimes in pleasant weather it was a consolation to look upon the cow's pranks as an intelligent attempt to play hide and seek, and as the child had no playmates she lent herself to this amusement with a good deal of zest. Though this chase had been so long that the wary animal herself had given an unusual signal of her whereabouts, Sylvia had only laughed when she came upon Mistress Moolly at the swamp-side, and urged her affectionately homeward with a twig of birch leaves. The old cow was not inclined to wander farther, she even turned in the right direction for once as they left the pasture, and stepped along the road at a good pace. She was quite ready to be milked now, and seldom stopped to browse. Sylvia wondered what her grandmother would say because they were so late. It was a great while since she had left home at half past five o'clock, but everybody knew the difficulty of making this errand a short one. Mrs. Tilley had chased the hornéd torment too many summer evenings herself to blame any one else for lingering, and was only thankful as she waited that she had Sylvia, nowadays, to give such valuable assistance. The good woman suspected that Sylvia loitered occasionally on her own account; there never was such a child for straying about out-of-doors since the world was made! Everybody said that it was a good change for a little maid who had tried to grow for eight years in a crowded manufacturing town, but, as for Sylvia herself, it seemed as if she never had been alive at all before she came to live at the farm. She thought often with wistful compassion of a wretched dry geranium that belonged to a town neighbor.

" 'Afraid of folks,' " old Mrs. Tilley said to herself, with a smile, after she had made the unlikely choice of Sylvia from her daughter's houseful of children, and was returning to the farm. " 'Afraid of folks,' they said! I guess she won't be troubled no great with 'em up to the old place!" When they reached the door of the lonely house and stopped to unlock it, and the cat came to purr loudly, and rub against them, a deserted pussy, indeed, but fat with young robins, Sylvia whispered that this was a beautiful place to live in, and she never should wish to go home.

The companions followed the shady wood-road, the cow taking slow steps, and the child very fast ones. The cow stopped long at the brook to drink, as if the pasture were not half a swamp, and Sylvia stood still and waited, letting her bare feet cool themselves in the shoal water, while the great twilight moths struck softly against her. She waded on through the brook as the cow moved away, and listened to the thrushes with a heart that beat fast with pleasure. There was a stirring in the great boughs overhead. They were full of little birds and beasts that seemed to be wide-awake, and going about their world, or else saying good-night to each other in sleepy twitters. Sylvia herself felt sleepy as she walked along. However, it was not much farther to the house, and the air was soft and sweet. She was not often in the woods so late as this, and it made her feel as if she were a part of the gray shadows and the moving leaves. She was just thinking how long it seemed since she first came to the farm a year ago, and wondering if everything went on in the noisy town just the same as when she was there; the thought of the great red-faced boy who used to chase and frighten her made her hurry along the path to escape from the shadow of the trees.

Suddenly this little woods-girl is horror-stricken to hear a clear whistle not very far away. Not a bird's whistle, which would have a sort of friendliness, but a boy's whistle, determined, and somewhat aggressive. Sylvia left the cow to whatever sad fate might await her, and stepped discreetly aside into the bushes, but she was just too late. The enemy had discovered her, and called out in a very cheerful and persuasive tone, "Halloa, little girl, how far is it to the road?" and trembling Sylvia answered almost inaudibly, "A good ways."

She did not dare to look boldly at the tall young man, who carried a gun over his shoulder, but she came out of her bush and again followed the cow, while he walked alongside.

"I have been hunting for some birds," the stranger said kindly, "and I have lost my way, and need a friend very much. Don't be afraid," he added gallantly. "Speak up and tell me what your name is, and whether you think I can spend the night at your house, and go out gunning early in the morning."

Sylvia was more alarmed than before. Would not her grandmother consider her much to blame? But who could have foreseen such an accident as this? It did not appear to be her fault, and she hung her head as if the stem of it were broken, but man-

aged to answer "Sylvy," with much effort when her companion
again asked her name.

Mrs. Tilley was standing in the doorway when the trio came
into view. The cow gave a loud moo by way of explanation.
"Yes, you'd better speak up for yourself, you old trial!
Where'd she tucked herself away this time, Sylvy?" Sylvia kept
an awed silence; she knew by instinct that her grandmother did
not comprehend the gravity of the situation. She must be mis-
taking the stranger for one of the farmer-lads of the region.

The young man stood his gun beside the door, and dropped a
heavy game-bag beside it; then he bade Mrs. Tilley good-evening,
and repeated his wayfarer's story, and asked if he could have a
night's lodging.

"Put me anywhere you like," he said. "I must be off early in
the morning, before day; but I am very hungry, indeed. You can
give me some milk at any rate, that's plain."

"Dear sakes, yes," responded the hostess, whose long slumber-
ing hospitality seemed to be easily awakened. "You might fare
better if you went out on the main road a mile or so, but you're
welcome to what we've got. I'll milk right off, and you make
yourself at home. You can sleep on husks or feathers," she prof-
fered graciously. "I raised them all myself. There's good pastur-
ing for geese just below here towards the ma'sh. Now step
round and set a plate for the gentleman, Sylvy!" And Sylvia
promptly stepped. She was glad to have something to do, and she
was hungry herself.

It was a surprise to find so clean and comfortable a little
dwelling in this New England wilderness. The young man had
known the horrors of its most primitive housekeeping, and the
dreary squalor of that level of society which does not rebel at
the companionship of hens. This was the best thrift of an old-
fashioned farmstead, though on such a small scale that it seemed
like a hermitage. He listened eagerly to the old woman's quaint
talk, he watched Sylvia's pale face and shining gray eyes with
ever growing enthusiasm, and insisted that this was the best supper he had eaten for a month; then, afterward, the new-made

friends sat down in the doorway together while the moon came up.

Soon it would be berry-time, and Sylvia was a great help at picking. The cow was a good milker, though a plaguy thing to keep track of, the hostess gossiped frankly, adding presently that she had buried four children, so that Sylvia's mother, and a son (who might be dead) in California were all the children she had left. "Dan, my boy, was a great hand to go gunning," she explained sadly. "I never wanted for pa'tridges or gray squer'ls while he was to home. He's been a great wand'rer, I expect, and he's no hand to write letters. There, I don't blame him. I'd ha' seen the world myself if it had been so I could."

"Sylvia takes after him," the grandmother continued affectionately, after a minute's pause. "There ain't a foot o' ground she don't know her way over, and the wild creatur's counts her one o' themselves. Squer'ls she'll tame to come an' feed right out o' her hands, and all sorts o' birds. Last winter she got the jay-birds to bangeing here, and I believe she'd 'a' scanted herself of her own meals to have plenty to throw out amongst 'em, if I hadn't kep' watch. Anything but crows, I tell her, I'm willin' to help support,—though Dan he went an' tamed one o' them that did seem to have reason same as folks. It was round here a good spell after he went away. Dan an' his father they didn't hitch,—but he never held up his head ag'in after Dan had dared him an' gone off."

The guest did not notice this hint of family sorrows in his eager interest in something else.

"So Sylvy knows all about birds, does she?" he exclaimed, as he looked round at the little girl who sat, very demure but increasingly sleepy, in the moonlight. "I am making a collection of birds myself. I have been at it ever since I was a boy." (Mrs. Tilley smiled.) "There are two or three very rare ones I have been hunting for these five years. I mean to get them on my own ground if they can be found."

"Do you cage 'em up?" asked Mrs. Tilley doubtfully, in response to this enthusiastic announcement.

"Oh, no, they're stuffed and preserved, dozens and dozens of them," said the ornithologist, "and I have shot or snared every one myself. I caught a glimpse of a white heron three miles from here on Saturday, and I have followed it in this direction. They have never been found in this district at all. The little white heron, it is," and he turned again to look at Sylvia with the hope of discovering that the rare bird was one of her acquaintances.

But Sylvia was watching a hop-toad in the narrow footpath.

"You would know the heron if you saw it," the stranger continued eagerly. "A queer tall white bird with soft feathers and long thin legs. And it would have a nest perhaps in the top of a high tree, made of sticks, something like a hawk's nest."

Sylvia's heart gave a wild beat; she knew that strange white bird, and had once stolen softly near where it stood in some bright green swamp grass, away over at the other side of the woods. There was an open place where the sunshine always seemed strangely yellow and hot, where tall, nodding rushes grew, and her grandmother had warned her that she might sink in the soft black mud underneath and never be heard of more. Not far beyond were the salt marshes and beyond those was the sea, the sea which Sylvia wondered and dreamed about, but never had looked upon, though its great voice could often be heard above the noise of the woods on stormy nights.

"I can't think of anything I should like so much as to find that heron's nest," the handsome stranger was saying. "I would give ten dollars to anybody who could show it to me," he added desperately, "and I mean to spend my whole vacation hunting for it if need be. Perhaps it was only migrating, or had been chased out of its own region by some bird of prey."

Mrs. Tilley gave amazed attention to all this, but Sylvia still watched the toad, not divining, as she might have done at some calmer time, that the creature wished to get to its hole under the doorstep, and was much hindered by the unusual spectators at that hour of the evening. No amount of thought, that night, could decide how many wished-for treasures the ten dollars, so lightly spoken of, would buy.

The next day the young sportsman hovered about the woods, and Sylvia kept him company, having lost her first fear of the friendly lad, who proved to be most kind and sympathetic. He told her many things about the birds and what they knew and where they lived and what they did with themselves. And he gave her a jack-knife, which she thought as great a treasure as if she were a desert-islander. All day long he did not once make her troubled or afraid except when he brought down some unsuspecting singing creature from its bough. Sylvia would have liked him vastly better without his gun; she could not understand why he killed the very birds he seemed to like so much. But as the day waned, Sylvia still watched the young man with loving admiration. She had never seen anybody so charming and delightful; the woman's heart, asleep in the child, was vaguely thrilled by a dream of love. Some premonition of that great power stirred and swayed these young foresters who traversed the solemn woodlands with soft-footed silent care. They stopped to listen to a bird's song; they pressed forward again eagerly, parting the branches,—speaking to each other rarely and in whispers; the young man going first and Sylvia following, fascinated, a few steps behind, with her gray eyes dark with excitement.

She grieved because the longed-for white heron was elusive, but she did not lead the guest, she only followed, and there was no such thing as speaking first. The sound of her own unquestioned voice would have terrified her,—it was hard enough to answer yes or no when there was need of that. At last evening began to fall, and they drove the cow home together, and Sylvia smiled with pleasure when they came to the place where she heard the whistle and was afraid only the night before.

II

Half a mile from home, at the farther edge of the woods, where the land was highest, a great pine-tree stood, the last of its generation. Whether it was left for a boundary mark, or for what reason, no one could say; the woodchoppers who had felled its mates were dead and gone long ago, and a whole forest of sturdy trees, pines and oaks and maples, had grown again. But the stately head of this old pine towered above them all and made a landmark for sea and shore miles and miles away. Sylvia knew it well. She had always believed that whoever climbed to the top of it could see the ocean; and the little girl had often laid her hand on the great rough trunk and looked up wistfully at those dark boughs that the wind always stirred, no matter how hot and still the air might be below. Now she thought of the tree with a new excitement, for why, if one climbed it at break of day, could not one see all the world, and easily discover whence the white heron flew, and mark the place, and find the hidden nest?

What a spirit of adventure, what wild ambition! What fancied triumph and delight and glory for the later morning when she could make known the secret! It was almost too real and too great for the childish heart to bear.

All night the door of the little house stood open, and the whippoorwills came and sang upon the very step. The young sportsman and his old hostess were sound asleep, but Sylvia's great design kept her broad awake and watching. She forgot to think of sleep. The short summer night seemed as long as the winter darkness, and at last when the whippoorwills ceased, and she was afraid the morning would after all come too soon, she stole out of the house and followed the pasture path through the woods, hastening toward the open ground beyond listening with a sense of comfort and companionship to the drowsy twitter of a half-awakened bird, whose perch she had jarred in passing. Alas, if the great wave of human interest which flooded for the first time this dull little life should sweep away the satisfactions of an existence heart to heart with nature and the dumb life of the forest!

There was the huge tree asleep yet in the paling moonlight, and small and hopeful Sylvia began with utmost bravery to mount to the top of it, with tingling, eager blood coursing the channels of her whole frame, with her bare feet and fingers, that pinched and held like birds claws to the monstrous ladder reaching up, up, almost to the sky itself. First she must mount the white oak tree that grew alongside, where she was almost lost among the dark branches and the green leaves heavy and wet with dew; a bird fluttered off its nest, and a red squirrel ran to and fro and scolded pettishly at the harmless housebreaker. Sylvia felt her way easily. She had often climbed there, and knew that higher still one of the oak's upper branches chafed against the pine trunk, just where its lower boughs were set close together. There, when she made the dangerous pass from one tree to the other, the great enterprise would really begin.

She crept out along the swaying oak limb at last, and took the daring step across into the old pine-tree. The way was harder than she thought; she must reach far and hold fast, the sharp dry twigs caught and held her and scratched her like angry talons, the pitch made her thin little fingers clumsy and stiff as she went round and round the tree's great stem, higher and higher upward. The sparrows and robins in the woods below were beginning to wake and twitter to the dawn, yet it seemed much lighter there aloft in the pine-tree, and the child knew that she must hurry if her project were to be of any use.

The tree seemed to lengthen itself out as she went up, and to reach farther and farther upward. It was like a great main-mast to the voyaging earth; it must truly have been amazed that morning through all its ponderous frame as it felt this determined spark of human spirit creeping and climbing from higher branch to branch. Who knows how steadily the least twigs held themselves to advantage this light, weak creature on her way! The old pine must have loved his new dependent. More than all the hawks, and bats, and moths, and even the sweet-voiced thrushes, was the brave, beating heart of the solitary gray-eyed child. And the tree stood still and held away the winds that June morning while the dawn grew bright in the east.

Sylvia's face was like a pale star, if one had seen it from the ground, when the last thorny bough was past, and she stood trembling and tired but wholly triumphant, high in the tree-top.

Yes, there was the sea with the dawning sun making a golden dazzle over it, and toward the glorious east flew two hawks with slow-moving pinions. How low they looked in the air from that height when before one had only seen them far up, and dark against the blue sky. Their gray feathers were as soft as moths; they seemed only a little way from the tree, and Sylvia felt as if she too could go flying away among the clouds. Westward, the woodlands and farms reached miles and miles into the distance; here and there were church steeples, and white villages; truly it was a vast and awesome world.

The birds sang louder and louder. At last the sun came up bewilderingly bright. Sylvia could see the white sails of ships out at sea, and the clouds that were purple and rose-colored and yellow at first began to fade away. Where was the white heron's nest in the sea of green branches, and was this wonderful sight and pageant of the world the only reward for having climbed to such a giddy height? Now look down again, Sylvia, where the green marsh is set among the shining birches and dark hemlocks; there where you saw the white heron once you will see him again; look, look! a white spot of him like a single floating feather comes up from the dead hemlock and grows larger, and rises, and comes close at last, and goes by the landmark pine with steady sweep of wing and outstretched slender neck and crested head. And wait! wait! do not move a foot or a finger, little girl, do not send an arrow of light and consciousness from your too eager eyes, for the heron has perched on a pine bough not far beyond yours, and cries back to his mate on the nest, and plumes his feathers for the new day!

The child gives a long sigh a minute later when a company of shouting cat-birds comes also to the tree, and vexed by their fluttering and lawlessness the solemn heron goes away. She knows his secret now, the wild, light, slender bird that floats and wavers, and goes back like an arrow presently to his home in the green world beneath. Then Sylvia, well satisfied, makes her perilous way down again, not daring to look far below the branch she stands on, ready to cry sometimes because her fingers ache and her lamed feet slip. Wondering over and over again what the stranger would say to her, and what he would think when she told him how to find his way straight to the heron's nest.

"Sylvy, Sylvy!" called the busy old grandmother again and again, but nobody answered, and the small husk bed was empty, and Sylvia had disappeared.

The guest waked from a dream, and remembering his day's pleasure hurried to dress himself that it might sooner begin. He was sure from the way the shy little girl looked once or twice yesterday that she had at least seen the white heron, and now she must really be persuaded to tell. Here she comes now, paler than ever, and her worn old frock is torn and tattered, and smeared with pine pitch. The grandmother and the sportsman stand in the door together and question her, and the splendid moment has come to speak of the dead hemlock-tree by the green marsh.

But Sylvia does not speak after all, though the old grandmother fretfully rebukes her, and the young man's kind appealing eyes are looking straight into her own. He can make them rich with money; he has promised it, and they are poor now. He is so well worth making happy, and he waits to hear the story she can tell.

No, she must keep silence! What is it that suddenly forbids her and makes her dumb? Has she been nine years growing, and now, when the great world for the first time puts out a hand to her, must she thrust it aside for a bird's sake? The murmur of the pine's green branches is in her ears, she remembers how the white heron came flying through the golden air and how they watched the sea and the morning together, and Sylvia cannot speak; she cannot tell the heron's secret and give its life away.

Dear loyalty, that suffered a sharp pang as the guest went away disappointed later in the day, that could have served and followed him and loved him as a dog loves! Many a night Sylvia heard the echo of his whistle haunting the pasture path as she came home with the loitering cow. She forgot even her sorrow at the sharp report of his gun and the piteous sight of thrushes and sparrows dropping silent to the ground, their songs hushed and their pretty feathers stained and wet with blood. Were the birds better friends than their hunter might have been,—who can tell? Whatever treasures were lost to her, woodlands and summer-time, remember! Bring your gifts and graces and tell your secrets to this lonely country child!

JESSAMYN WEST

Little Jess and the Outrider

Little Jess hurriedly shoved the food, the knife, and the New Testament into the cave he had hollowed out for them in the strawstack, then started on the run for the house. Halfway there he caught sight of his father and slowed to a walk. They met by the windmill.

His father set the basket of apples he was carrying on the ground and said, "I've been picking up windfalls. Thy mother said if I'd bring her enough summer sweetings she'd make us a batch of apple dumplings."

His father said no more, but Little Jess knew what he was thinking. He was thinking, *Now, it's thy turn to tell me what thee's been doing.* And Little Jess wasn't going to do it. For a moment he couldn't think of a single word he could safely say. Lately, every word he said seemed, in spite of himself, to have some connection with his secret. Finally he remembered the weather.

"It's a fine day, isn't it, Father?"

Was it fine? He took a quick look at the sky to see what kind of day, besides being hot, it was. The July sky seemed bigger than usual, blown up by the hot air the way a bladder is. Hard-looking clouds were piled up like boulders around the horizon, leaving the upper part of the sky unusually empty, blue, and faraway.

His father accepted the weather as a topic of conversation. "We need rain," he said. Then he picked up one of the windfalls and chomped into it.

Little Jess winced. "Green apples on an empty stomach will give thee a stomach ache." This was terribly near his secret, and his father seemed to suspect it, for he asked:

"How did thee come by that piece of information, Son? First-hand experience?"

It wasn't first-hand, so Little Jess changed the subject. "The Methodists are having a protracted meeting," he said, trying to make news of what they had all been talking about for a week.

"Thee been over?" his father asked.

"I been by," he admitted.

"Good attendance?"

Little Jess nodded. It had looked as if all of southern Indiana had been crowded in under the round Methodist tent.

"That's fine," his father said. "This country could stand a religious revival."

"What's *revival* mean?"

He knew—and he didn't know. The other night, coming home from the woods, he'd stood outside the camp meeting and listened to a woman say she had experienced the second birth and could sin no more. He had tried to imagine what that would be like: to get up in the morning and know he couldn't do a bad thing if he wanted to! What a change that would be! What a rest!

"What's second birth?" he asked.

"One thing at a time," his father told him, finishing his apple and throwing away the core. "*Revived* means born again, a spiritual rebirth."

"All thy sins forgiven?"

"A clean slate."

"Has thee been revived?"

"I hope so. I been banking on it."

"Has thee had the second birth?"

His father's eyes flashed a look of further inquiry.

"Can thee sin?" Little Jess explained.

"Oh, yes," his father, now that he understood the question, answered heartily. "I can sin all right. No doubt about that."

"I heard a lady at the tent meeting say she was past all sin."

"Well," Jess said, "if she is, she's got to an enviable spot."

"I'd like to be like that."

"I misdoubt many achieve it, even among the Methodists. What we would not, we do. What we would, we never get done."

Hearing those words, Little Jess thought his father had the power to look into his heart. The breakfast bell, ringing, gave him an excuse to start for the house. He left the conversation, on the dead run.

"Don't thee hear the bell?" he called back over his shoulder, suggesting that, except for it, he'd like nothing better than to talk about sin and the second birth all morning.

They were all at the breakfast table when Jess sat down. He took his place at the end of the table opposite his wife, Eliza. The two big boys, Josh and Labe, sat together on one side; facing them were Little Jess and Mattie.

Josh's head was still bandaged where he'd knocked a piece out of it in the spill he'd taken off a cliff. He and the rest of the Home Guard had tried to stop what they thought was a night attack by Morgan, the rebel raider. It had turned out to be not Morgan at all but stock crossing the river, and Josh was touchy about having gone to war and got himself bashed up fighting cows. It was bad enough for a Quaker to go off to war—let alone to find out he had given up his principles for no better reason than to scare the neighbor's milk animals. But Jess didn't tease him or let anyone else. Josh was a boy who took everything seriously, especially his own mistakes.

Labe, on the other hand, hardly ever made a mistake. It wasn't that he tried very hard to avoid them, but Labe seemed to be always moving in the same direction as the day and its events. Now he was wading into the fried bread, dried-beef gravy, and stewed berries as if he'd completely forgotten that not more than ten days ago Morgan had been threatening them all with death and destruction.

At the beginning of the Morgan ruckus Little Jess had wanted, in spite of his nine years, to go off with Josh and shoot Johnny Rebs; though since then Jess had noted with interest that the youngest son had lost his taste for gunpowder and developed an interest in second birth and revivals.

Seventeen-year-old Mattie, limp as a dock leaf in full sun, eyes vacant of the present scene, sat drooping over her fried bread in a daytime dream of love.

Eliza, dove sleek as always, was less than usually dove plump. She seemed diminished under the big midsummer sky, whittled down by the heat and by the emotions of the past ten days.

Jess, after this assessment of his family, pushed his plate of nicely browned fried bread aside and voiced for them what he supposed were their feelings as well as his own.

"The bottom seems to have dropped out of things, don't it?"

"What's that thee said, Jess?" Eliza asked the question as if suspecting the worst, but reluctant to condemn a man on a single hearing.

Jess was a man who learned what he thought by listening to what he had to say. Sometimes he forgot that Eliza learned what he was thinking in the same way. And Eliza, though she was a Quaker minister and knew well enough that the world was filled with sin, thought there were some sins which weren't improved by mentioning. And Jess knew he had just mentioned one of them.

"I said," he told her reluctantly, "that the bottom seems to have dropped out of things."

"Why does thee say that, Jess?"

She knows well enough, Jess thought. *And I do too. It's dropped out because for a little while we had all the excitement of a war here in Jenning's County. And Quakers or not, there's*

*still enough old Adam in us all, Eliza included, to make us feel,
now that Morgan's gone, that life's slacked off. That we're
caught in a backwater. It ain't a pretty picture, nor one I cotton
to any more than Eliza. The idea of us all low-spirited because
there's no one left in shooting distance don't sit well with me
either. But pretty or not, it's a true picture, and Eliza knows it.*

Eliza wasn't a woman who wrinkled her brow or pulled
down her mouth when displeased, but a shadow, speaking to
Jess louder than words, came over her face saying, *Persuade me,
Jess, that we don't love violence this much.*

"Eliza," he reminded her, "I didn't say it was a good thing
or that I liked it."

The children had stopped their eating to listen, as they always
did when they saw that their parents were in opposition—partly
out of anybody's interest in a tug of war, partly out of anxiety.
They were on both sides of the argument. They lost, no matter
who won.

Intending neither defeat nor victory, only the truth, Jess
said, "Maybe it's not such a bad feeling to have, Eliza. Maybe it
might teach us not to build on sand—if we don't like the feeling
of foundations crumbling out from under our feet."

It was a statement meant to reconcile, to point out the fact
that black truths sometimes have silver linings. Jess never had a
chance to find out if it did this. No sooner were the words out of
his mouth than Little Jess jumped from his chair, shaking the
table so that the dishes rattled, and shot out the kitchen door.
They watched, through the open kitchen windows, his loping
passage across the back yard. Dust, even after he had disappeared
behind the barn, marked his route. They turned away from
the window to look at one another in wonder.

Labe said finally, "He ought to lift his feet higher if he's
going to run that fast."

Little Jess paused at the strawstack to grab the flour sack
which held the knife, the food, and the New Testament; but he
paused only, then resumed his loping run.

He had been waiting for what had happened at breakfast. Not that he had had any idea that talk of shifting sands and the bottom dropping out of things was what he needed to send him running off to Roy. But when you're of two minds, a single word can change the balance. It was a relief now to have only one mind, and only one worry: would he get there in time? It was a relief to be finished with weighing right and wrong.

It was late in the morning, already after six o'clock. There was no dew left on the grass to smart his scratches. He ran inside the rail fence that separated the cornfield from the woods. Dust squirted up from between his toes. Pigweed and dock and mullein were thick in the cornfield. In the excitement of Morgan's coming and the letdown of his passing them by, the corn had missed a hoeing. A crow sat on the scarecrow. It was the first time Little Jess had seen a thing like that. It stopped him in his tracks. Perhaps it was a sign sent to warn him, to say, "Turn back before it is too late." As if to deny this, the crow flapped away, cawing loudly. Little Jess ran the length of the field, then ducked under the fence into the woods.

The woods, in early morning sunlight, was made up of separate trees whose names he knew: sycamore, black walnut, beech, maple. Toward evening the woods was no longer trees, but a single dark and frightening thing; a thing that drew close about him, that listened and waited to pounce. There was nothing *in* the woods that frightened him, even at night: bobcats, owls, porcupines, black whip snakes, coons, and possums; he could outface any of these. But the woods itself, growing darker and quieter at the end of a sultry afternoon, scared him.

Ten days ago, on the afternoon after Morgan had given them the go-by, Little Jess had come to the woods on purpose to be scared. The bottom had dropped out of things, the way his father had said, and he had been hunting for something real to take its place; and there is nothing more real than being scared. He had come to the woods for that, and the woods hadn't failed him.

The afternoon had been warm but overcast. The clouds had been a nasty color, like something that had started out white but had spoiled. The light that came through them had been ugly. Even when he moved, flies had stuck to his arms and legs as if magnetized. The crows had cawed bloody murder. There was no wind, nothing moved, and yet there had been sounds in the woods. The spots on the trunks of the sycamores, when he looked at them, had looked right back, getting bigger and darker, the way eyes do when they examine you. Leaves, as big as hands and as yellow as a Chinaman's, let go and, without a breath of wind to guide them, floated right at him. When he began to run, cobwebs had broken around his face and then had tightened up like nets somebody was pulling as he tried to push his way clear. But he had kept on going, deeper and deeper—the woods was keeping its part of the bargain, and he wasn't going to be the first one to back out.

What hadn't been in the bargain was the man. He had been almost through the woods on the west side when he had caught sight of him. He had been finished with scares and was thinking about going home. Then the man had darted out from the edge of the woods which Little Jess faced, and crouching, so that he half crawled, half ran, reached the fence which separated the woods from the fields. There he had done something quick and fumbling which Little Jess, in his fright, had not been able to make out. After a minute or two the man had lurched back to the cover of the trees.

After imagining so many things, after coming to the woods on purpose to imagine things, Little Jess had at first thought the man might be imaginary. The fact that he had worn something which looked as if it might have started life as a Confederate uniform hadn't proved anything one way or another. A blood-thirsty Reb, prowling the countryside on the lookout for someone to kill, would be just the kind of man he would imagine.

Little Jess had then made himself a part of the woods; and the minute they were on the same side, the woods had stopped scaring him. Together he and the woods had watched the Reb:

first, to see if he was a Reb; then to see, Reb or no Reb, what he was going to do next. What he had done next was to lurch back once more to the woods, swaying and scurrying like a bear. Little Jess hadn't been surprised that a Reb should remind him of an animal—men who kept slaves and screamed like panthers when they went into battle. This time the man had crawled through the fence, and had moved along, still crouching and with his hands still moving in the bushes. Little Jess had crept nearer to see what this motion could be.

It had been the motion of blackberry picking and eating, of grabbing wild blackberries from the vines and of cramming them flat-handed into his mouth. His hands had moved so fast that what he ate must've been as much bugs and leaves and rottenness as berries.

As Little Jess stared, the man had suddenly lifted his head and they had looked into each other's eyes. Little Jess had been unable to move. For a minute the blackberry picker, too, had been frozen, stiff hand held unmoving at his mouth. Then, crouching and lurching forgotten, he had jumped the fence and made straight for Little Jess. It was exactly the way Little Jess had dreamed it in nightmares, face to face with a killer and unable to move. As he waited, the man, running toward him, had begun to fall. It had taken him a long time, as if he, too, were dreaming. First he had stopped running. Then he remained upright but tottering. Finally his knees had begun to buckle and he had gone down, not face first, but sidewise, pawing the air as if he had been getting handholds in some rotten material which gave way as fast as he grabbed it.

There he had lain, stretched out at Little Jess' feet, as still as death. Little Jess' first thought had been that he *was* dead. Then he had remembered that dead men don't groan; and the Reb was groaning like a man asleep, but sick. For a Reb, his looks had been disappointing. He had looked like a boy, any boy—Josh. It was a comedown. Little Jess had expected something more awful. Tail and horns would've been no surprise to him. This groaner had been nothing but a boy with a thin covering of dirty skin to hold his sharp bones together. Around his mouth and eyes skin was twitching. The calf of one leg was bandaged, and the stink probably came from whatever the bandage hid.

While Little Jess stared, the Reb, without opening his eyes, had said, "Go ahead and shoot."

The idea of a Reb thinking about getting shot instead of shooting had been more than Little Jess could take in at once.

"Shoot and get it over with," the Reb repeated.

"I don't want to shoot thee."

The Reb had opened his eyes at this. "What did you say?"

"I said I didn't want to shoot thee."

"You're a Yank, ain't you?"

Little Jess didn't think he was, but he had known what the Reb meant.

"I'm on the Union side."

The Reb had then hoisted himself on one elbow and had held himself there, wobbling, until he had taken a good look at Little Jess.

"You're nothing but a kid," he had said. Then he fell back, closed his eyes, and began, once more, to groan.

"Is thee sick?" Little Jess had asked.

"I ain't got measles or consumption, if that's what you mean," he had said, between groans.

"Thee's groaning."

"I'm just starved to death, that's all. I'm just dying of lack of food. And of being shot at. I can't get anything to eat but raw stuff and it goes right through me. I'm starving and my leg's all proud flesh and I can't hardly move, but I ain't sick."

"Is thee a soldier?"

"I used to be."

"Why did thee stop?"

"I didn't stop. The army stopped."

"What army?"

"Morgan's. I was with Morgan. I was scouting for Morgan.

I'm where Morgan was supposed to be. I don't know where he
went."

"We scared him off," Little Jess had said proudly.

"You can't scare Morgan."

"Where is he, then?"

The Reb hadn't been able to answer this. "He sure left me
in the lurch."

"Why don't thee surrender?"

"Who to? You?"

"I'll bring my father."

When he heard this the Reb had sat all the way up.

"Surrender and get put in a Union prison? I'd rather starve
to death out here in the woods."

The Reb had been worn out by that speech. He lay back and
put an arm over his eyes and didn't make a sound, but his mouth
quivered more than ever.

Little Jess had started to tiptoe away but the Reb had heard
him. "You going to fetch your father?"

"I don't know."

The Reb hadn't asked him any more questions about what
he was going to do, and it wouldn't have done him any good if
he had. Because Little Jess himself didn't know.

It wasn't until the middle of the night that he had known.
What he was going to do was to take some food to that starving
Reb. He had gone downstairs and crept about gathering up what
cooked food he could find: cold biscuits, leftover ham, fried
cakes, a whole custard pie.

He didn't have any trouble finding the Reb. He was right
where he had left him. There had been an old ragged last quarter
of a moon, almost shined out but with still enough light to show
him the Reb, curled up about the base of a big sycamore. For
company it must've been, mostly. The night wasn't cold. If the
Reb was surprised when Little Jess called to him, he didn't show
it. He just shoved himself up against the tree, and with that to
hold him up had begun to eat.

Little Jess had always heard that a starving person should

break his fast gradually, take little bites and chew them a long time. After he had watched the Reb for a while, he told him this.

The Reb had heard this too. "I figured there was enough here, so that if this came up I could start all over again."

He kept it all down, though, and after he had finished the pie and gone back to biscuits, he had said to Little Jess, "Why don't you sit down?"

Little Jess didn't mind sitting, if he could sit off at a distance. The Reb was smelling higher every minute.

The Reb seemed to know this. "Keep off to windward," he had advised.

Little Jess had done this and after he had got himself settled the Reb had said, "My name's Roy. What's yours?"

"Little Jess."

"Little Jess? You ain't so very little. And when I first seen you, you sure looked like a giant."

"They don't call me Little Jess because I'm little. They call me that because Jess is my father's name."

"I don't know your father. Seems funny to call you little somebody when you ain't very little. I'll just call you Jess, if you don't mind, since that's your name."

"It's my name all right." Still he felt strange without the "Little," like a person trying to sail under false colors. "My father's the real Jess."

"Ain't you real?"

"I'm real, but my father's the—"

"I know. You told me. How old are you, Jess?"

"Nine."

"Woods scare you at night?"

"*They* didn't bother me so much."

"What did bother you?"

"Taking stuff without asking, to give to an enemy."

"Enemy? I ain't your enemy."

"Thee would be, except thee got lost from Morgan."

"Well, I'm good and lost, all right. I'm no man's enemy now."

"Thee's a slaveowner and willing to kill to keep thy slaves."

"Slaveowner!" Roy had hooted. "I don't even know any slaveowners. And the killing in this war's all been coming my way so far."

"Thee's on their side, though."

Roy didn't try to deny this, and Little Jess had remembered what it was so easy to forget: that Roy wasn't just any hungry boy; he was a Reb and the enemy of good people everywhere.

"You coming back again?"

"I don't know. I ain't making any promises."

"I ain't asking for promises."

He hadn't been, and Little Jess felt shamefaced to have suggested it.

"I just don't know," he had apologized.

"I know you don't," Roy had answered. "And all I was going to say was that if you did come back, would you bring me some turpentine? I got worms in my leg and I don't like the idea of worms eating me, till I'm dead. I got an idea turpentine'll burn 'em out."

"If I come," Little Jess had promised, "I'll bring turpentine."

But he had turned to leave without saying good-by. He couldn't help feeling that it was dangerous to talk to Roy. Slaveowner, secessionist, killer. He could tell himself all this, not looking at Roy, and believe it. Then he'd look, and he couldn't make those names fit. The best thing he could do was just turn tail and run.

Roy, once again, had called after him, "You going to tell your father?"

"I don't know."

"You tell him and I'm as good as in prison. And in a Union prison is just as good as dead."

"I didn't say I would."

"You didn't say you wouldn't."

"I told thee the truth," Little Jess had yelled back, running desperately to get out of earshot before he'd make some promise he'd regret.

He never did tell Jess, though. The next night he had brought the bottle of turpentine along with the food and had watched uneasily while Roy doused his leg with it.

"What battle did thee get that in?" he had asked, looking at the wound.

"Battle? Battle of the chicken house. Farmer took a shot at me while I was trying to steal a chicken."

Little Jess' ideas of war were changing fast. The only two soldiers he knew, Roy and Josh, had got their wounds through pretty unwarlike accidents: stealing chickens and falling off a cliff.

After Roy had got over squirming from the pain of the turpentine, he had said to Little Jess, "Draw up your chair and join me in a snack." Pretending the woods was his house and the food Little Jess had brought had come out of his own private pantry.

It hadn't seemed polite to refuse, and after that Little Jess had always put some extra food in the sack for himself. What he and Roy had had for ten nights amounted to a bunch of mid-night picnics with a lot of gab and jokes—and serious talk too. When he wasn't with Roy, Little Jess was ashamed of the thief and traitor he'd become. But there was no use denying that, with Roy, Little Jess was about as happy as he had ever been.

The turpentine had killed the worms and healed the wound, just the way Roy had said it would. Now he was going to cut for home in Milledgeville, Georgia. Last night Little Jess had brought him an outfit of Josh's so's he could travel through Union territory without getting shot at any more than necessary.

Little Jess felt shy about coming face to face in daylight with a person to whom he'd said things he'd die rather than even mention to Labe or Josh. In the warm, dark nights he'd been able to talk of all the things he'd wondered about and wished for: wonderments and wishes Roy'd never once laughed at. Except for Roy's being a Reb he didn't know anyone he liked better.

When Little Jess got to Roy's hideout, Roy was already

dressed for his journey in Josh's clean clothes. He was washed and combed, sitting on a log eating an apple turnover he'd saved for his breakfast.

"What's the matter, Jess?" Roy asked. "Something wrong?"

Little Jess had come to like being called Jess. At home when they said, "Little Jess," he thought, *Roy don't call me "Little." To him I'm good-sized and the only Jess there is.*

"What you staring at?" Roy asked again.

"Thee," Little Jess answered.

"What's wrong with me?"

"I didn't expect thee to look so nice."

"Why not? I'm a real nice-looking feller when I'm cleaned up and don't stink."

"Thee looks nice enough to go to meeting," Little Jess said.

"Meeting?"

"Church."

"You a churchgoer?"

"My mother's a preacher."

Roy whistled. "I reckon you got to walk the straight and narrow?"

Little Jess didn't answer and Roy put his head on one side and said thoughtfully, "I don't reckon that made what you've been doing any easier."

It hadn't, but it was all over now and Roy had enough troubles ahead of him just getting home to Milledgeville without worrying about him.

After a while Roy asked, "Did you see your way clear to bringing what I asked for?"

Little Jess took the knife out of the flour sack and handed it to Roy. It was the one his father used at butchering time and called a "pigsticker." It was as heavy as a butcher knife, but longer and more tapering. Roy took it and balanced it in his hand.

"This is a good knife," he said finally.

Little Jess nodded. He'd heard his father say the same thing many a time.

Roy felt the edge with his thumb. "You sharpened it for me, didn't you?"

"No. Father keeps it sharp."

"Looky, Jess, I'm not going to chop anybody's head off with this."

"I never said thee was."

"That's what you think, though?"

"I think thee'd defend thyself."

"Don't you want me to?" Roy asked. "You wouldn't want me to stand stock-still and get killed without lifting a hand, would you?"

"No." But he didn't want Roy killing anybody with his father's knife either.

"Looky, Jess," Roy said, "I ain't going to kill or be killed. I ain't in the army any more. I'm just traveling, just going home. All I'm going to use this knife for is to whittle kindling and clean me a chicken or a squirrel—if I'm lucky enough to catch me one. And pick my teeth. And cut my fingernails."

Little Jess couldn't joke about it. "I hope so," he said stiffly. He put his hand in the bag and added, "I got something else for thee, Roy."

"Didn't pick me up a gun someplace, did you?"

What Little Jess had was the opposite of a gun. He pulled it out reluctantly. A few crumbs from the hunk of applesauce cake he'd put in the flour sack were sticking to it and he brushed them off.

"What's that you got?"

"It's a Bible," Little Jess said.

"For me?"

Little Jess nodded.

"A Bible!" Roy repeated. "Why, Jess, I ain't got no more use for a Bible than a hog has for a sidesaddle."

Little Jess didn't argue with him about his need.

"If thee takes the knife, thee has to take the Bible too," he said.

"I already *got* the knife," Roy reminded him.

"If thee keeps the knife, thee has to take the Bible."

"Why?"

Little Jess wasn't sure.

"You trying to make a Quaker out of me?"

"No." He didn't think Roy would ever be a Quaker and he didn't care whether he was or not. He only knew that if he was going to be passing out knives to Confederate soldiers, the Bible had to go with them. One would kind of offset the other, maybe.

"You expect me to read it?"

"No." Whether he read it or not was Roy's business, not his. All *he* had to do was to see that if Roy took the knife he took with it the Book that said it was wrong to use the knife. He was that much responsible.

He handed it over to Roy and Roy took it gingerly, turning it round about in his hands.

"It's got a nice feel," he said finally, "for a book."

He put the Bible to one side of him on the log—the knife was on the other—and reached for the flour sack.

"I reckon I got about everything I need now, short of a horse," he said.

Little Jess was pretty sure Roy wouldn't be without that for long, but he stood up without saying anything. He wanted to be the first to go.

Roy seemed to know this. "Jess," he said, "we had us some nice talks, didn't we? Some nice talks and some nice little old midnight feasts?"

"They was nice, Roy. And thee was nice too."

Roy said, "You saved my life, Jess."

Little Jess didn't want to talk about that. To save a Confederate's life might be all right, but to arm him afterward wasn't. And that's what he had done, in spite of all Roy's talk about nail paring and tooth picking.

"I better go now," Little Jess said.

"I wish I had something to give you," Roy told him. "But excepting a lock of my hair I ain't got a thing you didn't give me first. Look, I won't make any promises about reading this, but I won't throw it away either. I can promise you that much."

That's what he said; but what he was doing was to feel how nice an edge there was on his knife. Roy didn't know he was doing it, but Little Jess saw, and knew where Roy's heart was.

"Good-by, Roy," he said. "Good luck."

"Good-by, Jess," the Reb said. "The same to you."

Little Jess ran away from Roy without once turning around or waving. When he came out in their own cornfield he met, for the second time that morning, his father. His father had a straw hat on the back of his head and a hoe over his shoulder.

"Thee going to hoe, Father?" he asked, his heart heavy to be pulling the wool over his father's eyes, the way he had been doing—and still was.

"I was thinking about it. I was thinking a little hoeing wouldn't hurt me or the corn either. Nothing like a little sweat to wash away your sins."

Little Jess was too wrapped up in his own sins to worry about anyone else's—let alone his father's. In fact, it was unthinkable that his father had any.

"Thee don't sin, Father."

His father pushed his hat forward and shifted his hoe to the other shoulder. "I can hoe corn from now till doomsday and still be black."

Something hung in the air, some invitation to speak and unburden himself. But little Jess could not accept it.

"Can I help thee hoe, Father?"

His father skimmed a few pigweeds skillfully from the ground. Then he leaned on his hoe and, without speaking, searched his son's face for a spell.

"No," he said finally. "I got a couple of real field hands in Josh and Labe coming out to help me. Thee help thy mother. She'll make thee sweat, if sweat is what thee needs."

Little Jess managed to smile. Tomorrow was First Day and

his mother always did more cooking and cleaning than usual on the day before, so that First Day could be enjoyed in peace and quiet. His father, when Little Jess smiled, put a hand on his shoulder.

"If sweat will do it, thy mother has the cure."

Sweat wouldn't do it; though his mother kept him on the run, she couldn't cure him. He scoured case knives, picked up more windfalls, picked berries by the peck, washed the surrey, carried fruit jars up from the cellar for airing, scrubbed porches and stairs, front and back, churned, peeled apples till his thumb was raw and finally, ending the day in a real lather, cleaned out the henhouses. But his heart was heavier than ever. His sins were festering in him like boils that needed poulticing.

As long as Roy had been in the woods, dependent on him, the work of figuring out how to get food to him without anyone's catching on had kept his mind off his wrongdoing. Now that Roy was gone, he had plenty of time to think. And sweat didn't seem to hinder thinking at all.

They had supper early, so there'd be time for baths. Little Jess dried dishes for Mattie while Labe and Josh used the tub. Mattie didn't stop talking once, but Little Jess didn't have any idea what she was saying. His mind was on Roy, homeward bound with that pigsticker in his belt. Finally he ran out of dishes to dry and, looking up, discovered the reason. Mattie had stopped washing and was standing, hands on hips, staring at him.

"Thee needn't think for a minute, Little Jess Birdwell, that thee is fooling me," she said when she saw she had his attention. "I know what ails thee."

"*What* ails me?" he asked boldly. If she really knew, there was nothing to be gained by beating around the bush.

"Thee has a secret."

That was a fact. But if that was *all* she knew, she didn't know much.

"How can thee tell?" he asked cagily.

"Because I've got one too. A very deep precious secret."

Little Jess smiled to himself behind his dishcloth. He was out of danger. Everyone knew Mattie's secret. She was in love. When he put down the dishcloth, Mattie had forgotten all about him and was admiring her hands, covered with soapsuds gloves. Mattie admired everything about herself nowadays. She would stand stock-still in front of a mirror, discovering her own face and the fact that it was pretty. Now she was arching and flexing her hands so that flakes of foam fell off.

"Having a secret," she said, "is the most beautiful thing in the world."

That hadn't been Little Jess' experience, but all he said was, "Don't anyone else know thy secret?"

"Of course!" said Mattie. "What would be the fun of a secret all alone? What would be the point?"

She didn't expect any answer from Little Jess, which was a good thing, because all he could've said was, "It's true, it's true! A secret alone is a terrible thing."

After he'd finished his own bath, Little Jess went outdoors. His clothes felt smooth and fresh against his newly scrubbed body. His feet, in the grass, were as white as hands. His wet hair, combed damp, stayed in place, leaving his face exposed to the evening. The sky was a jumble of light and dark: dark clouds but with sunset light shining through their ragged edges. Fireflies had just begun to show. All about him in the warm night there was a soft humming and buzzing. Crickets and katydids weren't ready yet for night. He could smell the hay, and the cows, and even, he thought, the peaches ripening out in the orchard. Back in the house he had left, Mattie was singing "Annie Laurie." In the kitchen, before an open window, his mother was cutting his father's hair. His father, while this went on, was reading his paper and whistling softly.

He could hear his mother's voice, but not her words. What his father said carried better. "Eliza, thee just leave the reading to me and keep thy eyes on those shears."

Everyone else was happy. Only he was alone and unhappy— a liar and traitor. At this very minute Roy might be pulling his knife on a farmer who objected to having his chickens—or horses—stolen. When he thought of this, Little Jess began to run.

He ran in the direction of the tent meeting, as he'd known all along he would do if his secret got too much for him. He ran through the summer night until the tent-meeting songs drowned out the crickets, and the kerosene flares that lighted the tent-meeting grounds made the sky black. He came to the beech grove where the churchgoers left their rigs and saw the eyes of a horse, wild and fiery and accusing, shining at him through a chink opened up by a movement of leaves. Black tree shadows quivered on the ground. The congregation was singing "Washed in the Blood of the Lamb." Little Jess was glad to have arrived at the place where he could get rid of his secret.

In the midst of all the noise, all the shouting and praying, the amenning and hallelujahing, the singing and confessing, he thought he would be able to confess, without being particularly noticed. He ought to be able to rise, say he had sinned and was sorry, without anybody's attention being riveted on him, as it would be in Quaker meeting. God surely didn't care *where* he said he was sorry; and if he could get rid of his secret here, he wouldn't have to face his father.

The great round tent had its side flaps lashed up, opening it to the night. Little Jess had thought of the tent and the people who filled it as a wheel of light which, when he got near enough, would pick him up and whirl him fiercely upward; and as it whirled, his sins would surely fall away from him. Afterward the great wheel of prayer and light would gently lower him, happy and free of sin, to the ground. On the wheel's upward journey he would probably have to say what he had done, but in the general turmoil his words would not be much noted—and saying them would be as easy and natural as breathing. That, anyway, was the way he had thought of it.

The tent was just as round as he remembered, the light as yellow, the sounds as surely circling upward and upward. Tent and people did form a wheel, just as he had thought, and the wheel did go round. It threw off sparks. It turned faster and faster. It roared and clacked and hissed like the windmill when the east wind blew. But what he hadn't imagined was that this wheel, instead of sucking him into its whirl and lifting him higher and higher, would, instead, push him farther and farther away. But that was what it was doing, though.

He stood at the rim of light and his prayer was, *Pick me up! Pick me up!* But the wheel pushed him away. He thought that if he could get past the people at the edges of the tent the wheel would do the rest. But the wheel began to turn so fast that all the openings at its edges closed. Sounds, so strange the hair on the back of his neck prickled like hog bristles, spilled over the rim of the wheel. He backed farther and farther away until he reached the beech grove and was in the midst of all the nervous fiery-eyed horses. From there he gazed back at the shining faces of the people who had made the whirling upward trip and had come back to earth happy and at ease. He longed to be one of them. But every time he moved toward the tent the wheel of light became a wheel of stone. Finally he sorrowfully turned his back on the revival meeting and started homeward. He would have to walk, he guessed, unforgiven all the rest of his life.

He saw his father, when he reached home, walking up and down the path between the currant bushes. He was barefooted, in his nightshirt, and once again was eating an apple. Little Jess was too heavy-hearted to say a word.

His father said, "We meet again."

Still Little Jess couldn't answer, and his father, gesturing with his apple, said, "A fine night for stars."

Little Jess managed to look upward. Away from the tent-meeting flares, the stars had come out again, soft summer stars with blurred edges like peonies about to shatter.

"Was thee waiting up for me?"

"In a way I was," his father said. "And in a way I wasn't. I come out as much as anything to enjoy the air after my bath. And to toughen up my feet. I don't like the idea of getting so dependent on shoes I couldn't go barefoot if I had to."

Little Jess still could say nothing.

"Did thee enjoy the tent meeting?"

"I just looked in. I didn't go."

"Thee wanted to go?"

Little Jess groaned. "I been doing wrong, Father," he said. "I've been doing the worst kind of things. I'm a traitor and a liar and a thief. Maybe a murderer by this time; I don't know. I reckon the best thing I can do is just leave home. Thee and Mother probably couldn't stand to live with anybody who's done the things I've done."

"I can stand to live with myself," Jess said.

"Thee hasn't done what I've done."

"I helped a poor starving boy get home to his folks."

At those words there was a silence in the night; the katydids and crickets were quiet; the stars and the house lights moved farther back, leaving a dark silent space around him and his father.

"Was he an enemy?" Little Jess asked, not breathing.

"I didn't think so. Though he had belonged to an army whose beliefs I don't share. But he wasn't born into this world our enemy, and he won't go out of it our enemy. And I didn't see any reason to believe that I ought to do him harm because for maybe two months out of his life he could be called by that name. No, he was a poor sick boy who needed food."

"*Thee* didn't take food without asking, for him."

"Everything I got belongs to thee, too, Little Jess."

"Thee didn't deceive anyone about what thee was doing."

"I reckon I deceived thee—some," his father said. "Didn't I?"

"Thee didn't give him a knife, Father," Little Jess said.

"I sharpened it," his father said. "I seen to it that it had a good edge on it, before thee took it out to Roy."

Roy! Little Jess' world was changing too fast for him to keep up with. He had to repeat his father's words to himself to make them real.

"Thee was doing it with me?" he said. "Helping Roy?"

"No, I wouldn't say that," his father told him. "The doing was thine. I don't take any credit to myself for those scary night

trips, and rustling up the right kind of grub. Or sitting out there
all hours of the night while Roy gabbed. I stood ready to help, if
thee needed help. But thee didn't need any help so far as I could
see. Thee saved a man's life all by thyself."

"Father," Little Jess said, "I liked Roy even if he was a Reb.
I liked him a lot. He listened to what I had to say."

"He was a good boy," Jess said. "I hope he lives to be a good
man." His father threw away his apple core and started toward
the house.

"Where's thee going, Father?"

Jess was already filling the biggest basin at the wash bench.
"Figure I better wash my feet off a little before I put them between thy mother's clean sheets."

"I better too," Little Jess said.

His father was sitting on the bench, one foot in the basin.
"Stick your feet in and I'll give them a rinse," he said. "Ain't
been too long since I was scrubbing you from head to toe."

Little Jess put one foot in the basin. "Father," he said, "do
you think Roy'll stab anyone with that knife?"

"No," his father said, "I don't. I figure Roy's had enough
kill-and-be-killed to last him a lifetime. I figure he's going to be
the most peaceful traveler on the roads till he's safe home and
can start putting that knife back to the work it was made for.
Let's have thy other foot."

"I don't suppose he'll read that Bible, though?"

"I misdoubt that myself," Jess said. "But that don't take
away from thy having had the thought to give it to him. I was
proud of thee for that. . . . There, that finishes thee."

Little Jess dried his feet on the grass while his father finished
his own washing.

"Thee feel all right now, Son?"

He said yes, though he didn't really feel all right. He loved
his father so much it hurt. He would have to figure some way to
use his love and he wanted to begin thinking about it right away.

"Good night, Father," he said and ran so lightly on his clean
feet up the stairs to bed, it was the next thing to flying.

WILLIAM FAULKNER

The Bear

He was ten. But it had already begun, long before that day when at last he wrote his age in two figures and he saw for the first time the camp where his father and Major de Spain and old General Compson and the others spent two weeks each November and two weeks again each June. He had already inherited then, without ever having seen it, the tremendous bear with one trap-ruined foot which, in an area almost a hundred miles deep, had earned for itself a name, a definite designation like a living man.

He had listened to it for years: the long legend of corncribs rifled, of shoats and grown pigs and even calves carried bodily into the woods and devoured, of traps and deadfalls overthrown and dogs mangled and slain, and shotgun and even rifle charges delivered at point-blank range and with no more effect than so many peas blown through a tube by a boy—a corridor of wreckage and destruction beginning back before he was born, through which sped, not fast but rather with the ruthless and irresistible deliberation of a locomotive, the shaggy tremendous shape.

It ran in his knowledge before ever he saw it. It looked and towered in his dreams before he even saw the unaxed woods where it left its crooked print, shaggy, huge, red-eyed, not ma-levolent but just big—too big for the dogs which tried to bay it, for the horses which tried to ride it down, for the men and the bullets they fired into it, too big for the very country which was its constricting scope. He seemed to see it entire with a child's complete divination before he ever laid eyes on either—the doomed wilderness whose edges were being constantly and punily gnawed at by men with axes and plows who feared it because it was wilderness, men myriad and nameless even to one another in the land where the old bear had earned a name, through which ran not even a mortal animal but an anachronism, indomitable and invincible, out of an old dead time, a phantom, epitome and apotheosis of the old wild life at which the puny humans swarmed and hacked in a fury of abhorrence and fear, like pygmies about the ankles of a drowsing elephant: the old bear solitary, indomitable and alone, widowered, childless, and absolved of mortality—old Priam reft of his old wife and having outlived all his sons.

Until he was ten, each November he would watch the wagon containing the dogs and the bedding and food and guns and his father and Tennie's Jim, the Negro, and Sam Fathers, the Indian, son of a slave woman and a Chickasaw chief, depart on the road to town, to Jefferson where Major de Spain and the others would join them. To the boy, at seven, eight, and nine, they were not going into the Big Bottom to hunt bear and deer, but to keep yearly rendezvous with the bear which they did not even intend to kill. Two weeks later they would return, with no trophy, no head and skin. He had not expected it. He had not even been afraid it would be in the wagon. He believed that even after he was ten and his father would let him go too, for those two weeks in November, he would merely make another one, along with his father and Major de Spain and General Compson and the others, the dogs which feared to bay at it and the rifles and shotguns which failed even to bleed it, in the yearly pageant of the old bear's furious immortality.

Then he heard the dogs. It was in the second week of his first time in the camp. He stood with Sam Fathers against a big oak beside the faint crossing where they had stood each dawn for nine days now, hearing the dogs. He had heard them once before, one morning last week—a murmur, sourceless, echoing through the wet woods, swelling presently into separate voices which he could recognize and call by name. He had raised and cocked the gun as Sam told him and stood motionless again while the uproar, the invisible course, swept up and past and faded; it seemed to him that he could actually see the deer, the buck, blond, smoke-colored, elongated with speed, fleeing, vanishing, the woods, the gray solitude, still ringing even when the cries of the dogs had died away.

"Now let the hammers down," Sam said.

"You knew they were not coming here too," he said.

"Yes," Sam said. "I want you to learn how to do when you didn't shoot. It's after the chance for the bear or the deer has done already come and gone that men and dogs get killed."

"Anyway," he said, "it was just a deer."

Then on the tenth morning he heard the dogs again. And he readied the too-long, too-heavy gun as Sam had taught him, before Sam even spoke. But this time it was no deer, no ringing chorus of dogs running strong on a free scent, but a moiling yapping an octave too high, with something more than indecision and even abjectness in it, not even moving very fast, taking a long time to pass completely out of hearing, leaving them some-where in the air that echo, thin, slightly hysterical, abject, almost grieving, with no sense of a fleeing, unseen, smoke-colored, grass-eating shape ahead of it, and Sam, who had taught him first of all to cock the gun and take position where he could see every-where and then never move again, had himself moved up beside him; he could hear Sam breathing at his shoulder and he could see the arched curve of the old man's inhaling nostrils.

"Hah," Sam said. "Not even running. Walking."

"Old Ben!" the boy said. "But up here!" he cried. "Way up here!"

"He do it every year," Sam said. "Once. Maybe to see who in camp this time, if he can shoot or not. Whether we got the dog yet that can bay and hold him. He'll take them to the river, then he'll send them back home. We may as well go back, too; see how they look when they come back to camp."

When they reached the camp the hounds were already there, ten of them crouching back under the kitchen, the boy and Sam squatting to peer back into the obscurity where they huddled, quiet, the eyes luminous, glowing at them and vanishing, and no sound, only that effluvium of something more than dog, stronger than dog and not just animal, just beast, because still there had been nothing in front of that abject and almost painful yapping save the solitude, the wilderness, so that when the eleventh hound came in at noon and with all others watching—even old Uncle Ash, who called himself first a cook—Sam daubed the tattered ear and the raked shoulder with turpentine and axle grease, to the boy it was still no living creature, but the wilderness which, leaning for the moment down, had patted lightly once the hound's temerity.

"Just like a man," Sam said. "Just like folks. Put off as long as she could having to be brave, knowing all the time that sooner or later she would have to be brave to keep on living with herself, and knowing all the time beforehand what was going to happen to her when she done it."

That afternoon, himself on the one-eyed wagon mule which did not mind the smell of blood nor, as they told him, of bear, and with Sam on the other one, they rode for more than three hours through the rapid, shortening winter day. They followed no path, no trail even that he could see; almost at once they were in a country which he had never seen before. Then he knew why Sam had made him ride the mule which would not spook. The sound one stopped short and tried to whirl and bolt even as Sam got down, blowing its breath, and jerking and wrenching at the rein, while Sam held it, coaxing it forward with his voice, since he could not risk tying it, drawing it forward while the boy got down from the marred one.

Then, standing beside Sam in the gloom of the dying afternoon, he looked down at the rotted overturned log, gutted and scored with claw marks and, in the wet earth beside it, the print of the enormous warped two-toed foot. He knew now what he had smelled when he peered under the kitchen where the dogs huddled. He realized for the first time that the bear which had run in his listening and loomed in his dreams since before he could remember to the contrary, and which, therefore, must have existed in the listening and dreams of his father and Major de Spain and even old General Compson, too, before they began to remember in their turn, was a mortal animal, and that if they had departed for the camp each November without any actual hope of bringing its trophy back, it was not because it could not be slain, but because so far they had had no actual hope to.

"Tomorrow," he said.

"We'll try tomorrow," Sam said. "We ain't got the dog yet."

"We've got eleven. They ran him this morning."

"It won't need but one," Sam said. "He ain't here. Maybe he ain't nowhere. The only other way will be for him to run by accident over somebody that has a gun."

"That wouldn't be me," the boy said. "It will be Walter or Major or—"

"It might," Sam said. "You watch close in the morning. Because he's smart. That's how come he has lived this long. If he gets hemmed up and has to pick out somebody to run over, he will pick out you."

"How?" the boy said. "How will he know—" He ceased. "You mean he already knows me, that I ain't never been here before, ain't had time to find out yet whether I—" He ceased again, looking at Sam, the old man whose face revealed nothing until it smiled. He said humbly, not even amazed, "It was me he was watching. I don't reckon he did need to come but once."

The next morning they left the camp three hours before daylight. They rode this time because it was too far to walk, even the dogs in the wagon; again the first gray light found him in a place which he had never seen before, where Sam had placed him and told him to stay and then departed. With the gun which

was too big for him, which did not even belong to him, but to
Major de Spain, and which he had fired only once—at a stump on
the first day, to learn the recoil and how to reload it—he stood
against a gum tree beside a little bayou whose black still water
crept without movement out of a canebrake and crossed a small
clearing and into cane again, where, invisible, a bird—the big
woodpecker called Lord-to-God by Negroes—clattered at a dead
limb.

It was a stand like any other, dissimilar only in incidentals to
the one where he had stood each morning for ten days; a territory
new to him, yet no less familiar than that other one which, after
almost two weeks, he had come to believe he knew a little—the
same solitude, the same loneliness through which human beings
had merely passed without altering it, leaving no mark, no scar,
which looked exactly as it must have looked when the first an-
cester of Sam Fathers' Chickasaw predecessors crept into it and
looked about, club or stone ax or bone arrow drawn and poised;
different only because, squatting at the edge of the kitchen, he
smelled the hounds huddled and cringing beneath it and saw
the raked ear and shoulder of the one who, Sam said, had had to
be brave once in order to live with herself, and saw yesterday in
the earth beside the gutted log the print of the living foot.

He heard no dogs at all. He never did hear them. He only
heard the drumming of the woodpecker stop short off and knew
that the bear was looking at him. He never saw it. He did not
know whether it was in front of him or behind him. He did not
move, holding the useless gun, which he had not even had warning to cock and which even now he did not cock, tasting in his
saliva that taint as of brass which he knew now because he had
smelled it when he peered under the kitchen at the huddled dogs.

Then it was gone. As abruptly as it had ceased, the woodpecker's dry, monotonous clatter set up again, and after a while
he even believed he could hear the dogs—a murmur, scarce a
sound even, which he had probably been hearing for some time
before he even remarked it, drifting into hearing and then out

again, dying away. They came nowhere near him. If it was a
bear they ran, it was another bear. It was Sam himself who came
out of the cane and crossed the bayou, followed by the injured
bitch of yesterday. She was almost at heel, like a bird dog, making
no sound. She came and crouched against his leg, trembling, staring off into the cane.

"I didn't see him," he said. "I didn't, Sam!"

"I know it," Sam said. "He done the looking. You didn't
hear him neither, did you?"

"No," the boy said. "I—"

"He's smart," Sam said. "Too smart." He looked down at the
hound, trembling faintly and steadily against the boy's knee.
From the raked shoulder a few drops of fresh blood oozed and
clung. "Too big. We ain't got the dog yet. But maybe someday.
Maybe not next time. But someday."

So I must see him, he thought. *I must look at him.* Otherwise,
it seemed to him that it would go on like this forever, as it had
gone on with his father and Major de Spain, who was older than
his father, and even with old General Compson, who had been
old enough to be a brigade commander in 1865. Otherwise, it
would go on so forever, next time and next time, after and after
and after. It seemed to him that he could never see the two of
them, himself and the bear, shadowy in the limbo from which
time emerged, becoming time; the old bear absolved of mortality
and himself partaking, sharing a little of it, enough of it. And he
knew now what he had smelled in the huddled dogs and tasted
in his saliva. He recognized fear. *So I will have to see him*, he
thought, without dread or even hope. *I will have to look at him.*

It was in June of the next year. He was eleven. They were in
camp again, celebrating Major de Spain's and General Compson's
birthdays. Although the one had been born in September and
the other in the depth of winter and in another decade, they had
met for two weeks to fish and shoot squirrels and turkey and
run coons and wildcats with the dogs at night. That is, he and

Boon Hoggenback and the Negroes fished and shot squirrels and
ran the coons and cats, because the proved hunters, not only
Major de Spain and old General Compson, who spent those two
weeks sitting in a rocking chair before a tremendous iron pot of
Brunswick stew, stirring and tasting, with old Ash to quarrel with
about how he was making it and Tennie's Jim to pour whiskey
from the demijohn into the tin dipper from which he drank, but
even the boy's father and Walter Ewell, who were still young
enough, scorned such, other than shooting the wild gobblers
with pistols for wagers on their marksmanship.

Or, that is, his father and the others believed he was hunting
squirrels. Until the third day, he thought that Sam Fathers believed that too. Each morning he would leave the camp right after
breakfast. He had his own gun now, a Christmas present. He
went back to the tree beside the bayou where he had stood that
morning. Using the compass which old General Compson had
given him, he ranged from that point; he was teaching himself to
be a better-than-fair woodsman without knowing he was doing
it. On the second day he even found the gutted log where he had
first seen the crooked print. It was almost completely crumbled
now, healing with unbelievable speed, a passionate and almost
visible relinquishment, back into the earth from which the tree
had grown.

He ranged the summer woods now, green with gloom; if
anything, actually dimmer than in November's gray dissolution,
where, even at noon, the sun fell only in intermittent dappling
upon the earth, which never completely dried out and which
crawled with snakes—moccasins and water snakes and rattlers,
themselves the color of the dappling gloom, so that he would not
always see them until they moved, returning later and later, first
day, second day, passing in the twilight of the third evening the
little log pen enclosing the log stable where Sam was putting up
the horses for the night.

"You ain't looked right yet," Sam said.

He stopped. For a moment he didn't answer. Then he said

peacefully, in a peaceful rushing burst as when a boy's miniature dam in a little brook gives way, "All right. But how? I went to the bayou. I even found that log again. I—"

"I reckon that was all right. Likely he's been watching you. You never saw his foot?"

"I," the boy said—"I didn't—I never thought—"

"It's the gun," Sam said. He stood beside the fence, motionless —the old man, the Indian, in the battered faded overalls and the five-cent straw hat which in the Negro's race had been the badge of his enslavement and was now the regalia of his freedom. The camp—the clearing, the house, the barn and its tiny lot with which Major de Spain in his turn had scratched punily and evanescently at the wilderness—faded in the dusk, back into the immemorial darkness of the woods. *The gun*, the boy thought. *The gun.*

"Be scared," Sam said. "You can't help that. But don't be afraid. Ain't nothing in the woods going to hurt you unless you corner it, or it smells that you are afraid. A bear or a deer, too, has got to be scared of a coward the same as a brave man has got to be."

The gun, the boy thought.

"You will have to choose," Sam said.

He left the camp before daylight, long before Uncle Ash would wake in his quilts on the kitchen floor and start the fire for breakfast. He had only the compass and a stick for snakes. He could go almost a mile before he would begin to need the compass. He sat on a log, the invisible compass in his invisible hand, while the secret night sounds, fallen still at his movements, scurried again and then ceased for good, and the owls ceased and gave over to the waking of day birds, and he could see the compass. Then he went fast yet still quietly; he was becoming better and better as a woodsman, still without having yet realized it.

He jumped a doe and a fawn at sunrise, walked them out of the bed, close enough to see them—the crash of undergrowth, the white scut, the fawn scudding behind her faster than he had believed it could run. He was hunting right, upwind, as Sam had taught him; not that it mattered now. He had left the gun; of his own will and relinquishment he had accepted not a gambit, not a choice, but a condition in which not only the bear's heretofore inviolable anonymity but all the old rules and balances of hunter and hunted had been abrogated. He would not even be afraid, not even in the moment when the fear would take him completely—blood, skin, bowels, bones, memory from the long time before it became his memory—all save that thin, clear, immortal lucidity which alone differed him from this bear and from all the other bear and deer he would ever kill in the humility and pride of his skill and endurance, to which Sam had spoken when he leaned in the twilight on the lot fence yesterday.

By noon he was far beyond the little bayou, farther into the new and alien country than he had ever been. He was traveling now not only by the old, heavy, biscuit-thick silver watch which had belonged to his grandfather. When he stopped at last, it was for the first time since he had risen from the log at dawn when he could see the compass. It was far enough. He had left the camp nine hours ago; nine hours from now, dark would have already been an hour old. But he didn't think that. He thought, *All right. Yes. But what?* and stood for a moment, alien and small in the green and topless solitude, answering his own question before it had formed and ceased. It was the watch, the compass, the stick—the three lifeless mechanicals with which for nine hours he had fended the wilderness off; he hung the watch and compass carefully on a bush and leaned the stick beside them and relinquished completely to it.

He had not been going very fast for the last two or three hours. He went no faster now, since distance would not matter even if he could have gone fast. And he was trying to keep a bearing on the tree where he had left the compass, trying to complete a circle which would bring him back to it or at least intersect itself, since direction would not matter now either. But the tree was not there, and he did as Sam had schooled him—made the next circle in the opposite direction, so that the two patterns would bisect somewhere, but crossing no print of his own feet, finding the tree at last, but in the wrong place—no bush, no compass, no watch—and the tree not even the tree, because there was a down log beside it and he did what Sam Fathers had told him was the next thing and the last.

As he sat down on the log he saw the crooked print—the warped, tremendous, two-toed indentation which, even as he watched it, filled with water. As he looked up, the wilderness coalesced, solidified—the glade, the tree he sought, the bush, the watch and the compass glinting where a ray of sunlight touched them. Then he saw the bear. It did not emerge, appear; it was just there, immobile, solid, fixed in the hot dappling of the green and windless noon, not as big as he had dreamed it, but as big as he had expected it, bigger, dimensionless against the dappled obscurity, looking at him where he sat quietly on the log and looked back at it.

Then it moved. It made no sound. It did not hurry. It crossed the glade, walking for an instant into the full glare of the sun; when it reached the other side it stopped again and looked back at him across one shoulder while his quiet breathing inhaled and exhaled three times.

Then it was gone. It didn't walk into the woods, the undergrowth. It faded, sank back into the wilderness as he had watched a fish, a huge old bass, sink and vanish into the dark depths of its pool without even any movement of its fins.

He thought, *It will be next fall*. But it was not next fall, nor the next nor the next. He was fourteen then. He had killed his buck, and Sam Fathers had marked his face with the hot blood, and in the next year he killed a bear. But even before that accolade he had become as competent in the woods as many grown men with the same experience; by his fourteenth year he was a better woodsman than most grown men with more. There was no territory within thirty miles of the camp that he did not know—bayou, ridge, brake, landmark, tree, and path. He could have led anyone to any point in it without deviation, and brought them out again. He knew the game trails that even Sam Fathers did not know; in his thirteenth year he found a buck's bedding place, and unbeknown to his father he borrowed Walter Ewell's rifle and lay in wait at dawn and killed the buck when it walked back to the bed, as Sam had told him how the old Chickasaw fathers did.

But not the old bear, although by now he knew its footprints better than he did his own, and not only the crooked one. He could see any one of the three sound ones and distinguish it from any other, and not only by its size. There were other bears within these thirty miles which left tracks almost as large, but this was more than that. If Sam Fathers had been his mentor and the backyard rabbits and squirrels at home his kindergarten, then the wilderness the old bear ran was his college, the old male bear itself, so long unwifed and childless as to have become its own ungendered progenitor, was his alma mater. But he never saw it.

He could find the crooked print now almost whenever he liked, fifteen or ten or five miles, or sometimes nearer the camp than that. Twice while on stand during the three years he heard the dogs strike its trail by accident; on the second time they jumped it seemingly, the voices high, abject, almost human in hysteria, as on that first morning two years ago. But not the bear itself. He would remember that noon three years ago, the glade, himself and the bear fixed during that moment in the windless and dappled blaze, and it would seem to him that it had never happened, that he had dreamed that too. But it had happened. They had looked at each other, they had emerged from the wilderness old as earth, synchronized to the instant by something more than the blood that moved the flesh and bones which bore them, and touched, pledged something, affirmed something more lasting than the frail web of bones and flesh which any accident could obliterate.

Then he saw it again. Because of the very fact that he thought of nothing else, he had forgotten to look for it. He was still-hunting with Walter Ewell's rifle. He saw it cross the end of a long blowdown, a corridor where a tornado had swept, rushing through rather than over the tangle of trunks and branches as a locomotive would have, faster than he had ever believed it could move, almost as fast as a deer even, because a deer would have spent most of that time in the air, faster than he could bring the rifle sights with it. And now he knew what had been wrong during all the three years. He sat on a log, shaking and trembling as if he had never seen the woods before nor anything that ran them, wondering with incredulous amazement how he could have forgotten the very thing which Sam Fathers had told him and which the bear itself had proved the next day and had now returned after three years to reaffirm.

And now he knew what Sam Fathers had meant about the right dog, a dog in which size would mean less than nothing. So when he returned alone in April—school was out then, so that the sons of farmers could help with the land's planting, and at last his father had granted him permission, on his promise to be back in four days—he had the dog. It was his own, a mongrel of the sort called by Negroes a fyce, a ratter, itself not much bigger than a rat and possessing that bravery which had long since stopped being courage and had become foolhardiness.

It did not take four days. Alone again, he found the trail on the first morning. It was not a stalk; it was an ambush. He timed the meeting almost as if it were an appointment with a human being. Himself holding the fyce muffled in a feed sack and Sam Fathers with two of the hounds on a piece of a plowline rope, they lay downwind of the trail at dawn of the second morning. They were so close that the bear turned without even running, as if in surprised amazement at the shrill and frantic uproar of the released fyce, turning at bay against the trunk of a tree, on its hind feet; it seemed to the boy that it would never stop rising, taller and taller, and even the two hounds seemed to take a desperate and despairing courage from the fyce, following it as it went in.

Then he realized that the fyce was actually not going to stop. He flung, threw the gun away, and ran; when he overtook and grasped the frantically pinwheeling little dog, it seemed to him that he was directly under the bear.

He could smell it, strong and hot and rank. Sprawling, he looked up to where it loomed and towered over him like a cloud-burst and colored like a thunderclap, quite familiar, peacefully and even lucidly familiar, until he remembered: This was the way he had used to dream about it. Then it was gone. He didn't see it go. He knelt, holding the frantic fyce with both hands, hearing the abashed wailing of the hounds drawing farther and farther away, until Sam came up. He carried the gun. He laid it down quietly beside the boy and stood looking down at him.

"You've done seed him twice now with a gun in your hands," he said. "This time you couldn't have missed him."

The boy rose. He still held the fyce. Even in his arms and clear of the ground, it yapped frantically, straining and surging after the fading uproar of the two hounds like a tangle of wire springs. He was panting a little, but he was neither shaking nor trembling now.

"Neither could you!" he said. "You had the gun! Neither did you!"

"And you didn't shoot," his father said. "How close were you?"

"I don't know, sir," he said. "There was a big wood tick inside his right hind leg. I saw that. But I didn't have the gun then."

"But you didn't shoot when you had the gun," his father said. "Why?"

But he didn't answer, and his father didn't wait for him to, rising and crossing the room, across the pelt of the bear which the boy had killed two years ago and the larger one which his father had killed before he was born, to the bookcase beneath the mounted head of the boy's first buck. It was the room which his father called the office, from which all the plantation business was transacted; in it for the fourteen years of his life he had heard the best of all talking. Major de Spain would be there and

sometimes old General Compson, and Walter Ewell and Boon
Hoggenback and Sam Fathers and Tennie's Jim, too, were hunters, knew the woods and what ran them.

He would hear it, not talking himself but listening—the wilderness, the big woods, bigger and older than any recorded
document of white man fatuous enough to believe he had bought
any fragment of it or Indian ruthless enough to pretend that any
fragment of it had been his to convey. It was of the men, not
white nor black nor red, but men, hunters with the will and
hardihood to endure and the humility and skill to survive, and
the dogs and the bear and deer juxtaposed and reliefed against it,
ordered and compelled by and within the wilderness in the
ancient and unremitting contest by the ancient and immiti-
gable rules which voided all regrets and brooked no quarter,
the voices quiet and weighty and deliberate for retrospection
and recollection and exact remembering, while he squatted
in the blazing firelight as Tennie's Jim squatted, who stirred
only to put more wood on the fire and to pass the bottle from
one glass to another. Because the bottle was always present,
so that after a while it seemed to him that those fierce instants of
heart and brain and courage and wiliness and speed were concentrated and distilled into that brown liquor which not women, not
boys and children, but only hunters drank, drinking not of the
blood they had spilled but some condensation of the wild immortal spirit, drinking it moderately, humbly even, not with the
pagan's base hope of acquiring the virtues of cunning and
strength and speed, but in salute to them.

His father returned with the book and sat down again and
opened it. "Listen," he said. He read the five stanzas aloud, his
voice quiet and deliberate in the room where there was no fire
now because it was already spring. Then he looked up. The boy
watched him. "All right," his father said. "Listen." He read again,
but only the second stanza this time, to the end of it, the last two
lines, and closed the book and put it on the table beside him.
"She cannot fade, though thou hast not thy bliss, for ever wilt
thou love, and she be fair," he said.

"He's talking about a girl," the boy said.

"He had to talk about something," his father said. Then he said, "He was talking about truth. Truth doesn't change. Truth is one thing. It covers all things which touch the heart—honor and pride and pity and justice and courage and love. Do you see now?"

He didn't know. Somehow it was simpler than that. There was an old bear, fierce and ruthless, not merely just to stay alive, but with the fierce pride of liberty and freedom, proud enough of the liberty and freedom to see it threatened without fear or even alarm; nay, who at times even seemed deliberately to put that freedom and liberty in jeopardy in order to savor them, to remind his old strong bones and flesh to keep supple and quick to defend and preserve them. There was an old man, son of a Negro slave and an Indian king, inheritor on the one side of the long chronicle of a people who had learned humility through suffering, and pride through the endurance which survived the suffering and injustice, and on the other side, the chronicle of a people even longer in the land than the first, yet who no longer existed in the land at all save in the solitary brotherhood of an old Negro's alien blood and the wild and invincible spirit of an old bear. There was a boy who wished to learn humility and pride in order to become skillful and worthy in the woods, who suddenly found himself becoming so skillful so rapidly that he feared he would never become worthy because he had not learned humility and pride, although he had tried to, until one day and as suddenly he discovered that an old man who could not have defined either had led him, as though by the hand, to that point where an old bear and a little mongrel of a dog showed him that, by possessing one thing other, he would possess them both.

And a little dog, nameless and mongrel and many-fathered, grown, yet weighing less than six pounds, saying as if to itself, "I can't be dangerous, because there's nothing much smaller than I am; I can't be fierce, because they would call it just noise; I can't be humble, because I'm already too close to the ground to genuflect; I can't be proud, because, I wouldn't be near enough to it for anyone to know who was casting the shadow, and I don't even know that I'm not going to heaven, because they have already decided that I don't possess an immortal soul. So all I can be is brave. But it's all right. I can be that, even if they still call it just noise."

That was all. It was simple, much simpler than somebody talking in a book about a youth and a girl he would never need to grieve over, because he could never approach any nearer her and would never have to get any farther away. He had heard about a bear, and finally got big enough to trail it, and he trailed it four years and at last met it with a gun in his hands and he didn't shoot. Because a little dog—But he could have shot long before the little dog covered the twenty yards to where the bear waited, and Sam Fathers could have shot at any time during that interminable minute while Old Ben stood on his hind feet over them. He stopped. His father was watching him gravely across the spring-rife twilight of the room; when he spoke, his words were as quiet as the twilight, too, not loud, because they did not need to be because they would last. "Courage, and honor, and pride," his father said, "and pity, and love of justice and of liberty. They all touch the heart, and what the heart holds to becomes truth, as far as we know the truth. Do you see now?"

Sam, and Old Ben, and Nip, he thought. And himself too. He had been all right too. His father had said so. "Yes, sir," he said.